On With The Show

MARKS & SPENCER

On With the Show

100 Years at Balmoral

by

Alf McCreary

Royal Ulster Agricultural Society
1996

First published 1996 for The Royal Ulster Agricultural Society
The King's Hall, Balmoral, Belfast, Northern Ireland
by W&G Baird Ltd., Caulside Drive, Antrim BT41 2RS

ISBN 1 870157 22 2

Frontispiece: Aerial view of King's Hall and Balmoral Showgrounds

Designed by Rodney Miller Associates, Belfast.

Printed by W&G Baird Ltd., Antrim.

BUCKINGHAM PALACE.

Agricultural societies are peculiarly British institutions and they have played a most important part in the development of agriculture ever since the industrial revolution introduced new technologies into the ancient business of farming.

The Royal Ulster Agricultural Society is no exception and during its hundred years at the Balmoral showgrounds it has been giving splendid service to the farmers and rural communities of Northern Ireland. The Balmoral Show has become the 'shop window' of agriculture in the Province and it has enabled the urban population to gain an insight into the working of the agricultural industry.

This history of the first hundred years at Balmoral might have been rather dry and full of statistics, but it is more to do with the people - and the characters - whose commitment has made the Society the great enterprise that it is today.

I have happy memories of visits to Balmoral and I am sure that it is the energy and enthusiasm of its members and management that has carried it through the 'troubles' of the last quarter century so successfully.

To complete a century of service in the one location is a great achievement, but I am confident that the Society has even more to offer in the future.

Philip

HRH Prince Philip, the Duke of Edinburgh,
Patron, Royal Ulster Agricultural Society 1996

Foreword

Anyone coming fresh to the history of the Royal Ulster Agricultural Society and its antecedents will soon realise that this is an institution with roots deeply embedded in the history of Ulster itself. The story itself is clear, after the ambiguities of the Society's early origins are recognised, but frequently the narrative branches out to many topics that are not strictly agricultural. These include entertainment, sport, commercial exhibitions and even significant affairs of State.

The names of the famous and successful are part of this story, ranging from King Edward VII to Queen Elizabeth II and many other "Royals", from Sir Edward Carson to John Major in the world of politics, to Louis Armstrong, Mantovani and Sir Cliff Richard in entertainment, to World Champion boxers from Rinty Monaghan to Barry McGuigan, and many others as well. There are also the stories of the scarcely-known people whose hard work and commitment to Balmoral and the RUAS have made them very special institutions, not only locally, but much further afield.

The Society, of course, is much older than the first Century of the Show at Balmoral which falls in 1996, and in one sense its story is timeless because, like the seasons themselves, the RUAS and Balmoral and its people move steadily on. The essence of that story, of course, is agriculture but anyone who believes that it is exclusively concerned with farming is in for a surprise!

My journey in researching and writing this book has taken me into all kinds of fascinating corners of history and of contemporary life, and I will never look at Balmoral and The King's Hall again without a feeling of warmth and regard for the place and what it represents.

Finally, I trust that you, too, will enjoy your own journey between the lines of this most fascinating section of the history of Ulster and its people.

Alf McCreary
Belfast
26 September 1995

Acknowledgements

The author wishes to acknowledge the help of many people who made this publication possible. They include Bill Yarr, Chief Executive and Secretary of the RUAS for his dedicated, thorough and unobtrusive help; Hilary McCreary for her support as yet another literary journey unfolded; Pauline Allen for her skill in preparing the manuscript; Patricia Trueman, Rhonda Duncan and Mervyn Dinsmore for assisting with the collection of voluminous research material; Dr Margaret Crawford of Queen's University for her help in supplying pictures and captions on the Great Famine; Lord Lowry for some background material on Show Jumping; Barry Niblock and Leslie Martin of the Department of Agriculture for help with material associated with World War II, Mike McComb for sourcing an 1896 copy of *Belfast Weekly News*, many members of Council who provided old photographs and Ralph Dobson for the use of a cartoon; Jack Magowan and Michael Drake of the *Belfast Telegraph*; freelance journalist Michael Slavin, and Dr 'Jimmy' Young former Permanent Secretary of the Department of Agriculture, are all deserving of special thanks for their distinctive contributions, as is former BBC journalist John Johnston for the use of a number of pre-recorded interviews.

The author and publishers would also like to thank the following for the use of material from their publications – the Editors of the *Belfast Telegraph*, the *News Letter*, the *Irish News*, *Farmweek*, *Farmers' Weekly*, *Horse and Hound*, the *Daily Mail*, the *Daily Telegraph*, and those whose scholarly and literary sources are quoted, and duly acknowledged in the text. Finally, the author would like to thank all those who are not mentioned by name but whose contribution and help is greatly appreciated, while the RUAS is grateful to the Belfast City Council, the Department of Agriculture, the *News Letter*, The Gibson Trust and all those whose financial assistance, directly or in kind, helped to defray the costs of this book.

In particular the author and publisher would like to thank Bryan McCabe of W&G Baird Limited, the printers, and Arnold Gormley of Rodney Miller Associates, the designers, for their skill and assistance in the production and presentation of this volume.

Contents

ORIGINS *Chapter 1*

THE NORTH-EAST AGRICULTURAL ASSOCIATION, which staged the first Balmoral Show in 1896, grew out of an earlier body – the North East Agricultural Association of Ireland which was formed in 1854. The January 1933 edition of the *Balmoral Bulletin* appeared to put beyond doubt that the North East Society (formed in 1826) had some connection, however remote, with the North East Association. The basis of this was a letter written in January 1926 by the Earl of Clanwilliam with which he included a framed copy of a notice concerning a meeting to form the North East Society. This notice together with a copy of the initial subscription list still adorns the walls of the Chief Executive's office at Balmoral. The meeting took place in the Commercial Buildings, Belfast on 4 April 1826 and was chaired by the third Marquis of Downshire, Arthur Blundell Hill who was noted for having taken a leading part in the development of the farming industry not only in Ulster but across the island of Ireland. Obviously not everyone accepted that the North East Society and the North East Agricultural Association were connected, for whilst all the current official badges clearly show the founding year as 1826, the Society's seal remains unchanged at 1854. The economic historian David L Armstrong states that a North-West of Ireland Agricultural Association was formed in 1821, and that it was largely responsible for the foundation in 1826 of an Agricultural School in Templemoyle in County Londonderry. This, he believes, was the beginning of agricultural education in Ireland where, in the 19th Century, a lack of knowledge of the principles of sound husbandry and an uncritical preference for the traditional methods of farming were serious obstacles to agricultural progress. Up to 1850 some 800 pupils from Ireland, England and Scotland had passed through the School but, largely as a result of financial difficulties brought about by the Great Famine, the School was then attached to the

TELEPHONE,
SLOANE 3757.

51, CADOGAN SQUARE,
S.W.1.

30. 1. 26

Dear Sir

I have much Pleasure in forwarding you the enclosed Notice which I have had framed and which relates to the institution of an Agricultural Society in Ulster in 1826 and which was evidently the forerunner of the Royal Ulster Agricultural Society, and I would beg you to ask the President & Members of the Society to do me the honour of accepting it as it may prove of interest in view of the celebration of the Society's Centenary —

Yours truly

Clanwilliam

To The Secretary
The Royal Ulster Agricultural Society

The Earl of Clanwilliam's letter of 30 January 1926 suggesting that the North East Society, which was formed in 1826, was the forerunner of the RUAS.

Board of Education. After 1850 the School declined in importance, and it was closed down in 1866. Incidentally, the diet of the pupils is of interest. The Report for 1857 notes:

> For breakfast they had fourteen ounces of bread and one pint of coffee each. For dinner on Monday and Tuesday each received a half pound of pickled beef, a quarter stone of potatoes and another vegetable; on Wednesday, Friday and Saturday, two ounces of butter, a quarter stone of potatoes, one pint of sweet

NORTH EAST SOCIETY.

AT a Meeting of the Noblemen and Gentlemen of the Counties of Down, Antrim and Armagh, held in the Commercial Buildings, pursuant to Public Notice, on Tuesday the 4th day of April, for the purpose of forming an AGRICULTURAL SOCIETY—

The MARQUIS of DOWNSHIRE in the Chair,

It was Resolved—That this Meeting do constitute and form itself into an AGRICULTURAL SOCIETY, for those Counties, to be called the NORTH EAST SOCIETY.

That a Committee of the following Gentlemen be requested to solicit Subscriptions from the landed Proprietors, and all others interested in such a Society, in their respective Counties :—

ARTHUR CRAWFORD, CHARLES BROWNLOW, ALEXANDER M'NEILE,
WILLIAM E. REILLY, WILLIAM VERNER, JOHN ROWAN,
N. D. CROMMELIN, WILLIAM BLACKER, HENRY ADAIR.

That the following Gentlemen be appointed Honorary Secretaries, until the next General Meeting, and be requested to act until such Meeting :—

ARTHUR MONTGOMERY, GEORGE MACARTNEY, THOMAS EVANS.

That an immediate Subscription be commenced, and a list opened by those persons present for Subscriptions and Donations, and copy do remain after the Meeting with each of the Honorary Secretaries.

That the lowest Subscription be £2, 2s.

That the forgoing Committee be appointed, and requested to meet as often as necessary previous to the next General Meeting, to form a table of such Officers, Rules, and Regulations as may be required for the government of the Society, and submit the same at the General Meeting.

That the Committee be requested to hold their first Meeting at KERNS's Hotel, Belfast, on the second Wednesday in May, at Twelve o'Clock.

That a General Meeting of the Society be held in the Commercial Buildings, Belfast, on Tuesday next succeeding the Summer Assizes of Down, to receive the Report of the Committee, appoint Officers, and transact such other business as may appear necessary.

That this Society do Dine together on the day of the General Meeting, at KERNS's Hotel.

Signed DOWNSHIRE, CHAIRMAN.

Lord DOWNSHIRE having left the Chair, and CHARLES BROWNLOW, Esq. M. P. being called thereto,

It was Resolved—That the Thanks of this Meeting be given to Lord DOWNSHIRE, for his handsome conduct in the Chair.

C. BROWNLOW.

SUBSCRIPTION LIST

OF THE

NORTH EAST SOCIETY,

OPENED AT A MEETING HELD APRIL 4, 1826.

	ANNUAL.			DONATION.		
	£	s	d.	£	s,	d,
Downshire - - - - -	50	0	0	50	0	0
Donegall - - - - -	50	0	0	50	0	0
Arthur Hill - - - - -	10	0	0	20	0	0
M. Forde - - - - -	30	0	0	50	0	0
C. Brownlow - - - -	30	0	0	50	0	0
Robert Bateson - - - -	20	0	0	20	0	0
J. W. Maxwell - - - -	10	0	0	10	0	0
William E. Reilly - - - -	2	2	0	5	0	0
George Macartney - - - -	10	10	0	20	0	0
N. D. Crommelin - - - -	3	3	0	5	0	0
Daniel Delacherois - - - -	3	3	0	5	0	0
John Echlin - - - -	2	2	0	5	0	0
John M'Cance - - - -	5	5	0	10	0	0
George A. Wray - - - -	2	2	0	0	0	0
Roger Hall - - - -	5	5	0	10	0	0
George Greer - - - -	3	3	0	5	0	0
Thomas Darly - - - -	2	2	0	5	0	0
J. L. Reilly - - - -	2	2	0	5	0	0
Acheson St. George - - - -	3	3	0	5	0	0
J Atkinson - - - - -	3	3	0	5	0	0
Robert Bradshaw - - - -	2	2	0	0	0	0
James Johnston - - - -	3	3	0	5	0	0
James S. Beggs - - - -	2	2	0	5	0	0
R. J. Thornton - - - -	2	2	0	5	0	0
Hugh Kennedy - - - -	2	0	0	5	0	0
C. Gregg - - - -	4	0	0	5	0	0
	£262	16	0	£360	5	0

BELFAST, PRINTED BY A. MACKAY JUN.

The Minute of the Meeting held on 4 April 1826 when the North East Society was formed. The list of subscriptions is also shown.

milk or buttermilk and another vegetable; on Thursday, a half pound of fresh beef, soup and potatoes and on Sunday three quarters of a pound of fresh beef stewed with pepper and onions and cabbage and other vegetables. For supper each was given ten ounces of bread and one pint of coffee.[1]

The efforts of the Board of Education had little immediate effect on the standards of cultivation because it was unable to provide educational facilities for the tenant farmers. Farming societies, however, had more success. They encouraged farmers to improve their methods by offering prizes for good cultivation and drainage, and by organising Shows to demonstrate the latest developments in implements and breeds of livestock. By 1849, there were 35 Societies in the North of Ireland affiliated to the Royal Agricultural Improvement Society of Ireland which had been founded in 1841. As well, there were a large number of independent Societies. A survey of *The Northern Whig* 1850 indicates the range of Societies in operation – on 15 January 1850 there are references to Ballymoney Farming Society, Londonderry District Farming Society, and Dungiven and Bovevagh Farming Society; on 2 February Dromore Farming Society organised a Ploughing Match; in February and March there were references to Antrim Union Farming Society, Coleraine Farming Society, and Dungannon Farming Society; on 1 August Carrickfergus and Kilroot Agricultural Society appointed a Committee to establish an Agricultural School and Model Farm, and also a Cattle Show on 8 September; and on 13 August the paper reported that the Dundrum and Ballykinlar Estates Farming Society had presented their first Cattle and Farming Show on 9 August 1850 in Dundrum in a walled field outside the town to which the Marquis of Downshire had sent a supply of livestock.

From our perspective it is important to remember that many of these local Societies were being formed at a time when the disastrous Irish famine was still fresh in folk memory. Professor JC Beckett notes: "Taking into account all the available evidence, we may reasonably assume that between 1845 and 1850 not far short of 1,000,000 people died, either of disease or of hunger, as a result of the Great Famine."[2] He further notes: "The ghastly and unmistakable terms in which the Great Famine had posed the land question lost their urgency when the immediate crisis was past; but the question itself remained and could not indefinitely be postponed; how was Irish agriculture to be improved to a point at which it could provide adequate support for the population dependent upon it?"[3]

The horrors of the Great Famine have been well-summarised. Dr Liam Kennedy, the historian, writes:

> Relatively few actually starved to death. Most were the victims of fever and dysentery, diseases which flourished under conditions of malnutrition, poor hygiene, and inadequate public health measures. One brief illustration of the degree of distress, and of efforts to contain the crisis, must suffice. The description relates to Castledawson in south Derry during the first hungry winter in Ulster (1846-47) and was written by a local gentleman: 'I do not exaggerate when I tell you that from the moment I open my hall door in the morning until dark, I have a crowd of women and children crying out for something to save them from starving . . . I have been obliged to turn my kitchen into a bakery and soup shop to enable me to feed the miserable children and mothers that cannot be sent away empty. So great is their distress that they actually faint on getting food into their stomachs . . . The gentry, the shopkeepers, the clergy are making every effort in their power to relieve the people, by subscriptions, and incessant attention, but what can be done when thousands are daily applying for one meal a day. We are also visited by hordes of wandering poor who come from the mountains . . .'[4]

It was against such a recent background, and a prevailing desire to improve agriculture, that a meeting was held in Hillsborough, on 21 September 1854. It was attended by The Marquis of Downshire (the fourth Marquis, known as "The Big Marquis"), the Very Rev Dean Stannus, Lisburn; John Waring Maxwell, Finnebrogue; AH Montgomery, Tyrella; H Stanley McClintock, Randalstown; SK Mulholland, Eglantine; SD Crommelin, Carrowdore Castle; Rev Dr Montgomery, Dunmurry; Jonathan Richardson, Glenmore; William Charley, Seymour Hill; and Fitzherbert Filgate, Hillsborough.

The Marquis of Downshire took the Chair, and it was "unanimously resolved that steps should be taken towards the formation of a Society, to be entitled 'The North-East Agricultural Association of Ireland,' embracing the counties of Down, Antrim, Armagh, and Monaghan, and having for its general objects, (1) the improvement of stock and farm produce by holding an annual show for their exhibition; (2) the encouragement of the manufacture of implements suitable to the North-eastern counties of Ireland; and (3) the dissemination of practical and useful knowledge connected with agriculture in its various branches."[5]

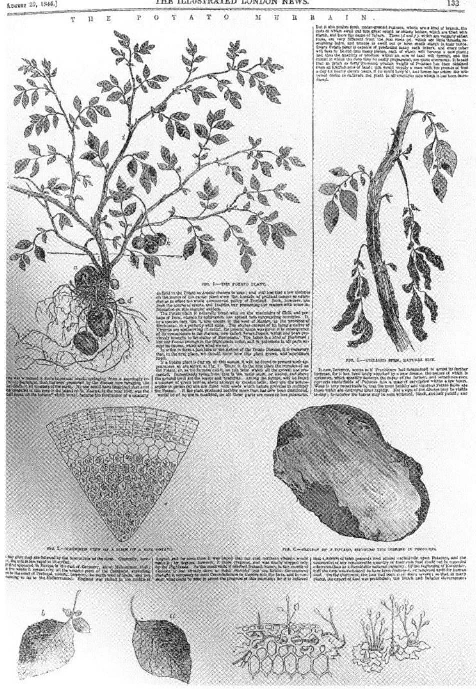

August 29, 1846.] THE ILLUSTRATED LONDON NEWS. 133

THE POTATO MURRAIN.

1

BOY AND GIRL AT CAHERA.

2

3

Famine Misery

(1) In the autumn of 1845 the Irish potato crop was attacked by ***phythophthora infestans*** (potato blight). At the time the pestilence was a mystery, though we now know that it was fungal disease, which spread with alarming speed, the spores being disseminated by wind, rain and mist. In appearance, blighted potato stalks turned black, the tubers rotted and the plant emitted an offensive odour.

(2) The atmosphere of the picture depicts misery and despair as the two children scour a barren field in search for a potato or two that evaded blight and escaped the eye of previous scavengers. The expression of the boy's face is pained and his stance is of one starved both of food and heat. His clothes, and those of the girl, are ragged.

(3) Driving cattle for rent at the height of the famine crisis. This engraving appeared in 1849 with the comment from the reporter that "It may serve to vary a little the miseries I have to portray".

(All photographs appeared in ***The Illustrated London News***.)

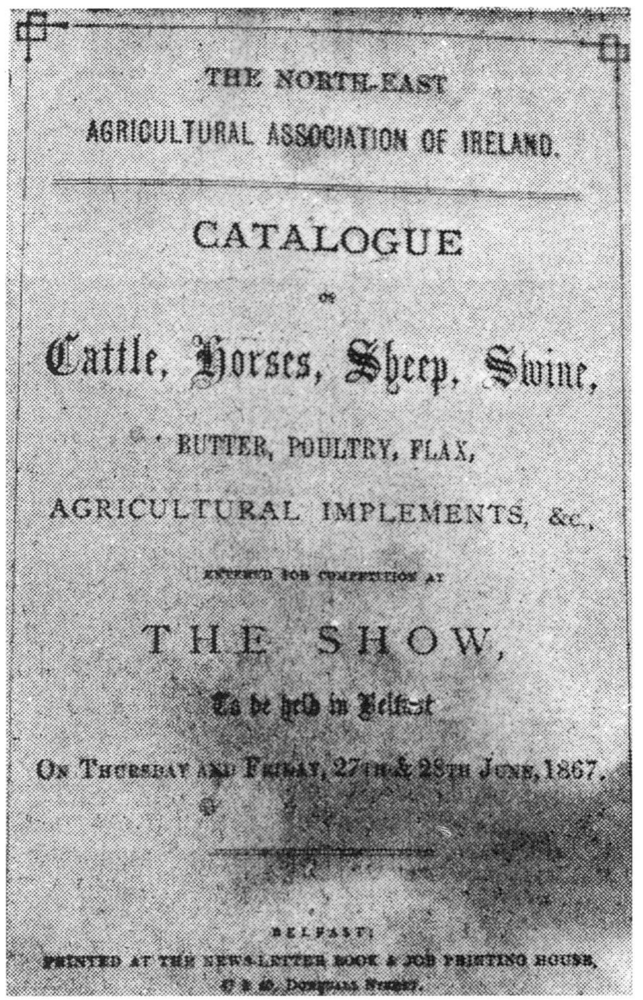

THE NORTH-EAST
AGRICULTURAL ASSOCIATION OF IRELAND.

CATALOGUE
OF
Cattle, Horses, Sheep, Swine,
BUTTER, POULTRY, FLAX,
AGRICULTURAL IMPLEMENTS, &c.,
ENTERED FOR COMPETITION AT
THE SHOW,
To be held in Belfast
ON THURSDAY AND FRIDAY, 27TH & 28TH JUNE, 1867.

BELFAST:
PRINTED AT THE NEWS-LETTER BOOK & JOB PRINTING HOUSE,

The catalogue cover for the the 1867 Show.

To carry out the resolution of the preliminary meeting, a general meeting took place in the Town Hall, Belfast on 20 October 1854. "The Big Marquis" again took the Chair and presided over a meeting of 85 others, including John Borthwick of Kilroot, who was later to become a senior figure in the Association. It was the same John Borthwick who gave long and distinguished service to the Belfast Saving Bank, which opened on 5 January 1816. He was Honorary Manager 1830-39, Resident Manager 1839-59 and Honorary Secretary 1860-76. By combining his business interests with service on bodies such as the North East Agricultural Association of Ireland, John Borthwick was not only typical of his time but also a forerunner of those who have given much time and expertise to the Royal Ulster Agricultural Society and its forebears over the years. John Borthwick was Treasurer of the Association until his death in 1878 when this role was taken over by the Northern Bank Ltd. The Northern had been the Association's bankers since its inception and have remained so ever since – a special relationship lasting 142 years.

At its meeting of 20 October, the Association passed 14 Resolutions. It decided that it would confine its activities "for the present, to the Counties of Down, Armagh and Antrim, including the County of the town of Carrickfergus." It also decided wisely, in the light of contemporary and later events, that "Subjects of political or religious controversy shall not be discussed at any of the meetings of this Association." Above all it decided that "The great object of this Association being the encouragement of practical farming, the competition for the money premiums of the Society shall be chiefly confined to working farmers, and others whose principal means of living is obtained from agriculture." Thus the new Association was confirmed in Belfast only some five years after the youthful Queen Victoria had come to the city with her Consort Prince Albert and had visited, among other places, the new Queen's College (now Queen's University) which had been established with two other Colleges at Cork and Galway in 1845.

The first Show of the Association was held in Belfast on the 23 and 24 August 1855 and it was generally regarded as a success. There were 506 entries for three sections, including 241 for the Farmers Class, 236 for the Amateur Class, and 29 implement stands. The prizes included 204 money premiums, amounting to £216, as well as 93 medals and 73 certificates. On Show

Belfast Corporation Markets, the venue for the Show from 1855 to 1895.

Night, a banquet was held at which the Marquis of Downshire presided. The 300 guests included the Lord Mayor of Belfast and representatives from the Churches, the professions and the business community. Despite the rejoicing at the success of the Show, there may have been many thoughts on matters of Empire much further afield, and notably on the Crimean War which was at its height in 1855.

At this time, the Show was held in the Belfast Corporation's grain, potato and vegetable markets in Chichester Street and the catalogue contains guidance on how to get there. It says: "The public will be admitted to the Showgrounds by the entrance to the grain market in Chichester Street. Admittance is two shillings."

Another comment reads: "Horses may be removed from the show yard for the night after six o'clock upon the owner depositing with the Secretary before five o'clock the sum of one pound for each as a guarantee that they shall be brought back before nine o'clock. In each case the deposit must be paid in actual cash."

From 1855 an Annual Show was organised till the turn of the century, when the Society decided to hold two Shows each year. The exception was in 1866, when no Show was held, due to an outbreak of rinderpest. In 1861, the North East Show merged with the Annual Show of the Royal Agricultural Society of Ireland. This was a peripetitic show held every four years in each of the four Provinces of Ireland. A similar situation occurred in 1872 when the combined Show was held on 7, 8 and 9 August 1872, in the Ormeau Park, Belfast. According to a report:

> The display in the livestock class was creditable, but in the whole fell short of what might have been expected. This, however, was accounted for by the fact that Foot and Mouth Disease existed among stock at that period to such an extent that the Government Veterinary Department deemed it incumbent upon them to appoint an Officer specially to attend the Show.[6]

There was a Winter Show of the Association in 1860, for fat stock, poultry, roots, cereals, flax, flax-seed, butter and cheese, but due to a lack of support this was discontinued.

By all accounts, the Shows were of great importance.

> They stimulated interest in agricultural matters and gave farmers an opportunity to study the latest developments in implements and to see fine quality livestock. The Shows were fully reported in the newspapers and were frequently the occasion of critical articles on the progress of agriculture in the region.[7]

The Association was not content to confine itself to organising Shows, and in 1857 decided to offer prizes for the best managed farms. Each County was divided into three districts, with six prizes allocated to each – three were for farms of more than 40 acres, and three for smaller farms. These competitions were withdrawn from 1867 "the entries having been much more limited than might reasonably have been expected."[8]

Despite the attempts to improve the standards of agriculture, there were those who took a hostile view of such developments. There was a great deal of agitation over land issues and some people believed that the rise of the farming Societies was a deliberate ploy to divert attention from the social and political upheaval of the day. In September 1859 there was a stern warning in *The Nation*:

> If landlords in various parts of the country pleased to amuse themselves with exhibitions of fat beasts and overgrown turnips and cabbages we should see nothing calling for particular comment in their conduct – provided always that they did not endeavour to induce a rack-rented tenantry, who have no secure tenure of their farms, to enter the lists with them, and provided they did not attempt as they invariably do, to identify the prosperity of the country with the fatness of their swine and the monstrosity of their vegetables.[9]

The Association was keen from the outset to encourage the display of agricultural implements and machinery. In 1870 there was a trial of mowing machines and double-furrow ploughs, held in the grounds of the Ulster Model Farm of the Board of Education situated on the Lisburn Road close to what was later to become Balmoral Showgrounds, and similar trials were held in 1871 and 1873. However "The Committee had been appealed to dispense with these exhibitions in consequence of the disadvantage under which manufacturers at a distance laboured in competing with those located in Belfast or the neighbourhood."[10]

The Association also made a significant contribution to the standardisation of weights and measures for agricultural produce. The lack of uniformity in this was a distinct disadvantage, and the Association carried out extensive research and placed the matter before Parliament which, in 1862, passed an Act adopting the Association's principle and included many of its detailed recommendations.

The success of the Association since its inception posed problems, however. For many years the Shows were held in the Belfast Corporation's Markets area, but with the increase in entries these premises became inadequate. In 1890, for example, there were 896 entries compared to 506 at the First Show in 1855. Therefore in 1891 the Association appealed to its members and the general public for funds to purchase new premises "which would afford more ample space for the Association's Shows, and more particularly for the development of its Horse Shows.[11] A special Permanent Show Yard Committee was appointed to identify suitable land for the proposed new premises and various sites were considered at Bloomfield, Fortwilliam Park, Andersonstown, Turf Lodge, Ulsterville, Castlereagh Road, Ballymacarret, Ormeau Road and Antrim Road. By far the most favoured however was land at Balmoral Park owned by Arthur Hamill of Trench House who was a Vice-President of the Association. He made an offer of 50 acres at £10/acre but the Show Yard Committee felt that such a size would be much too large for the purposes of the Association, bearing in mind that the combined area in the grain, potato and vegetable markets amounted to only 3 acres 2 roods and 17 perch! Eventually in 1894, the purchase of approximately 30 acres was agreed on a fee farm grant basis of £12.50 per acre. It was reported that "these grounds are in every way suitable for the purpose and most conveniently situated as regards tramway and railway accommodation."[12]

The agreed price was felt to be more than fair but Arthur Hamill's generosity did not stop there as in 1896 he presented a wonderful silver trophy, the Hamill Challenge Cup for competition in the Horse section. He also gave a donation of £500 towards the funds of the Association.

Up to this time, as the Association had no assets there was no real need for it to be incorporated. The purchase of a permanent Showground however signalled the necessity for such action. Following application to Her Majesty's Privy Council in Ireland, approval was given by Order in Council on 21 May 1894 for the North East Agricultural Association to become incorporated under the Educational Endowments (Ireland) Act 1885, and a Scheme was framed for the future government and management of the Endowments belonging to the Association.

The Scheme laid down that "the endowments shall be held by the Council upon trust to promote Agriculture in the Province of Ulster and chiefly in the Counties of Antrim, Down, Armagh and Monaghan by holding Agricultural Shows and by giving Agricultural instruction and by such other means as may from time to time be found expedient."

In the past century there have been a number of amendments to the original Scheme (in 1903, 1912, 1928, 1937, 1958, 1980 and 1984), and many of these were minor or enforced. In essence the import of the 1894 wording is still operative. One significant change to the objects, however, was to add "the promotion of Industries, Art, Sciences and Literature" (1937) but despite this, the promotion of Agriculture remains the major objective of the organisation.

With incorporation in place, and sufficient money raised or promised, plans were put in hand to develop the site, with a view to staging the first Show at Balmoral in June 1896. In August 1895 the Show Yard Committee inspected the site and were highly pleased with the sub soil – the only part requiring attention for bad drainage being that known as the "Bog Field". The Trotting Association in London was asked for advice on the size of a track which would be suitable for trotting and cycling.

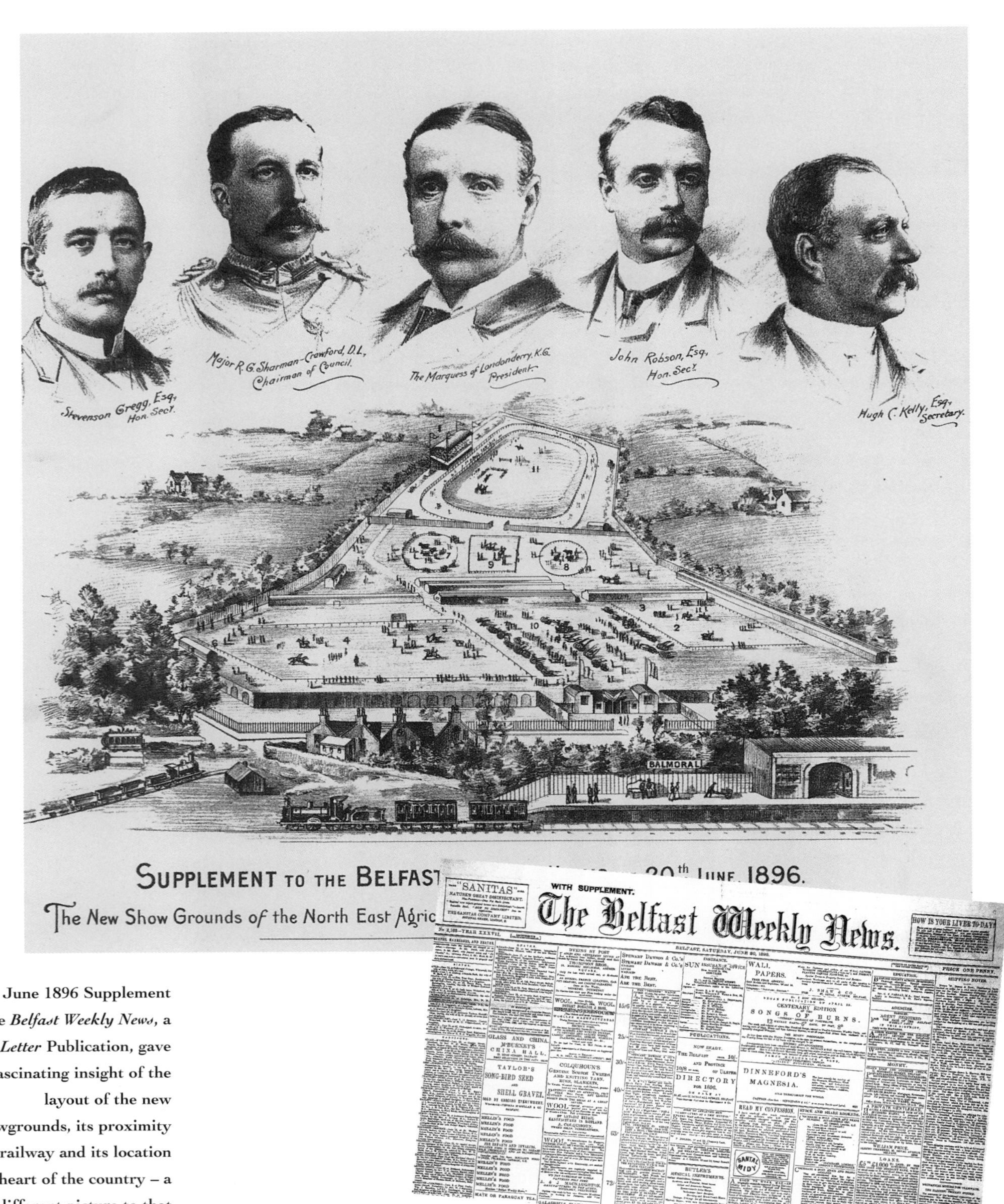

The June 1896 Supplement of the *Belfast Weekly News*, a *News Letter* Publication, gave a fascinating insight of the layout of the new Showgrounds, its proximity to the railway and its location in heart of the country – a much different picture to that of 1996.

Messrs R Graeme-Watt and Tulloch were appointed as architects and the levelling of the land was carried out by a Mr James McLarnon. In February 1896 tenders were sought for the enclosing of the 30 acre site, the erection of accommodation for stock, the laying of the arena track and the building of a Grand Stand.

In mid March 1896, the various appointed contractors started work – only twelve weeks prior to the opening of the first Show.

During that period there was frantic activity, as over three hundred workmen busied themselves to complete the task for the big day. Messrs McLaughlin & Harvey were entrusted with walling-in (with solid blocks) the boundary on the Lisburn Road and Balmoral Avenue. This wall still stands today. They also built a series of stables, one of which – 576 ft in length – is the building now known as the Londonderry Hall. Messrs Musgrave and Company of Ann Street completed the enclosure of the site with a corrugated iron fence and also built the Grand Stand at the Trotting track. The Grand Stand, now known as the Royal Stand, is still in use and immediately behind it can be seen part of the corrugation which, aided by numerous coats of paint not to mention patches, could still be termed as being part of the original fence.

Mr Hampden Shaw of Dublin was the engineer supervising the laying of the trotting track, which, oblong in shape, had a width of 40 ft (12 ft wider than that at Ballsbridge). There were three laps to the mile and the track could be converted into a cycle racing path modelled on the world famous track at Herne Hill.

The "gentlemen of the Press" were invited to see the progress being made towards the end of April 1896, and they expressed amazement at what had been achieved in such a short time. They expressed some doubt, however, that all would be ready for the opening day of the first Show at Balmoral (Wednesday, 17 June) – but it was! The cost of translating a series of green fields to a first-class agricultural Showground had amounted to £14,000!

After some 40 years of continued success in a turbulent era which had more than its fair share of upheaval and tragedy in the Irish Agriculture of the 19th Century, the Association was approaching a new century with a brand new site, the confidence of its past achievements and high hopes for the future.

The Hamill Challenge Cup was presented in 1896, for competition by middleweight hunters. It was won outright in 1906 by James Milling of Comber having had the winning exhibit three years in succession.

Mr Milling's daughter, Mrs Flo Carpenter, herself a competent and successful show jumper in the 1920's, "found" the cup when she was moving house in 1992. She decided that she wished to re-present the cup to the Society but not for competition. It was handed back at a special ceremony during the Annual Meeting in February 1993. The photograph shows Mr and Mrs Carpenter together with (centre) the then President (the late William E S Fullerton), the immediate Past President, James Pollock (right) and the Chief Executive Bill Yarr.

The cup is now proudly displayed in the trophy case in the foyer of the Balmoral Conference Centre.

(Photograph: Visuals Photography.)

Notes

1 An Economic History of Agriculture in Northern Ireland from 1850 – 1900 by David L Armstrong (Plunkett Foundation for Co-operative Studies 1989)
2 The Making of Modern Ireland (Faber and Faber p.343)
3 op.cit p.351
4 An Economic History of Ulster 1820-1939, edited by Liam Kennedy and Philip Ollerenshaw, and published by Manchester University Press; p.28
5 The North-East Agricultural Association, Ireland: Industrial and Agricultural (1901) p.119
6 North-East Agricultural Association op.cit p.123
7 David L Armstrong op.cit p.224
8 North-East Agricultural Association op.cit p.121
9 David L Armstrong op.cit p.222
10 North-East Agricultural Association op.cit p.122
11 Ibid p.123
12 Ibid p.123

(Top) A wide angle view of the Showgrounds at the 1897 Balmoral Show.

(Below) The most modern machinery of the day was exhibited at the 1897 Show.

THE ROYAL ULSTER AND BEYOND . . . *Chapter 2*

THE FIRST ANNUAL SHOW AT BALMORAL (the forty first Show organised by the North East Agricultural Association) was held on the 17, 18 and 19 of June 1896. It was "a memorable one, on account of its being the first held in the new premises, and also by its being extended to three days. The value of the prizes offered amounted to nearly £1,000, and the number of entries was a very great advance on that of any Show previously held by the Association".[1] There had been, of course, a three-day Show in 1872 in Ormeau Park, but this was in association with the Royal Agricultural Society of Ireland. The entry list in the first Balmoral Show in 1896 totalled 1,391, and was nearly three times that of the first North-East Agricultural Association of Ireland Show in 1855.

The details of the entries also reveal an interesting contrast. Between 1855 and 1896, the entries in the Shorthorn classes varied between 89 and 63, with a peak of 117 in 1878, while the Ayrshires ranged from 28 in 1855 to 30 in 1896, with a peak of 86 in 1864. The sheep entries remained steady, from 85 in 1855 to 105 in 1896, with a peak of 130 in 1890, as did the swine entries which stood at 45 in 1855 and 47 in 1896, with peaks of 77 in 1856 and 1862. The really significant and continuous growth was reflected in the number of entries in horses, and poultry and eggs. The former ranged from only 71 in 1855 to 486 in 1896 (the highest ever to that date), while the poultry and eggs increased from 59 in 1855 to 405 in 1896, which was also a record year. The total prize money more than quadrupled from the 1855 total of £216, and overall the organisers had reason to be pleased with the scope and success of the first Balmoral Show which reflected the rise in the influence of the Association since that first exploratory meeting in Hillsborough in September 1854. This success was reflected in Press reports that were full of praise - and written in the purple prose of a bye-gone age! *The Northern Whig* of Saturday, 20 June 1896 summed up:

> As was generally anticipated, yesterday was the popular day *par excellence* at the Show. Nearly ten thousand persons passed through the turnstiles, and, making allowance for season and subscribers ticket-holders, the Showground must have been visited by between fourteen and fifteen thousand people. These are figures which, together with the good returns on the first two days, should be highly gratifying to the promoters and friends of the Show, especially considering that the weather throughout was the reverse of favourable, and that the means of reaching the Show from the city have not yet been perfected. Everything considered, the patronage given by the public to the new venture is most satisfactory, and the result should encourage the Executive of the Association to pursue the bold and progressive policy which has met thus far with success. The aim should be to make Balmoral as popular in the North as Ballsbridge is in the South.
>
> There was nothing inviting about the weather in the forenoon yesterday. The skies looked lowering and threatening enough, but fortunately the rain held off until the tail of the proceedings in the jumping-ground, by which time almost everybody was thinking of going home, as the hour of closing the Showgrounds (five o'clock) was fast approaching. Unfortunately the wind-up was not as pleasant as could have been desired. A pelting downpour drove all but the hardiest from the exposed portion of the Grounds before the prizes in the chief jumping competition were awarded, and those who remained to see the result had little satisfaction for their pains, the placings on the board at the finish being singular enough to cause general surprise. The Show opened at nine o'clock in the morning, and from the first it was evident that there was going to be a record attendance. Each one of the frequent trains from the city to Balmoral brought a formidable contingent, and those coming from the other direction also conveyed many hundreds of visitors to the Show. Of the heavy batches of country people who came into the city by the Northern Counties and County Down Railways many patronised the tramway service, in which a great improvement was made as compared with the first day in "bunching" the cars and starting them in "squads" of three or four. Then of course the jarveys had their turn, and at the moderate fares fixed by agreement with the Association did a brisk trade.
>
> Between ten and twelve o'clock the vicinity of the showyard presented a very animated scene, and the turnstile keepers had a remarkably busy time. Inside the Ground one could not help being struck with the small proportion of the gentler sex among the country visitors compared with former years. This, however, was easily explained by the threatening character of the morning, following on the dampness of the past two days. Though there was a plenitude of mud in the showyard, the "going" for visitors was improved considerably by

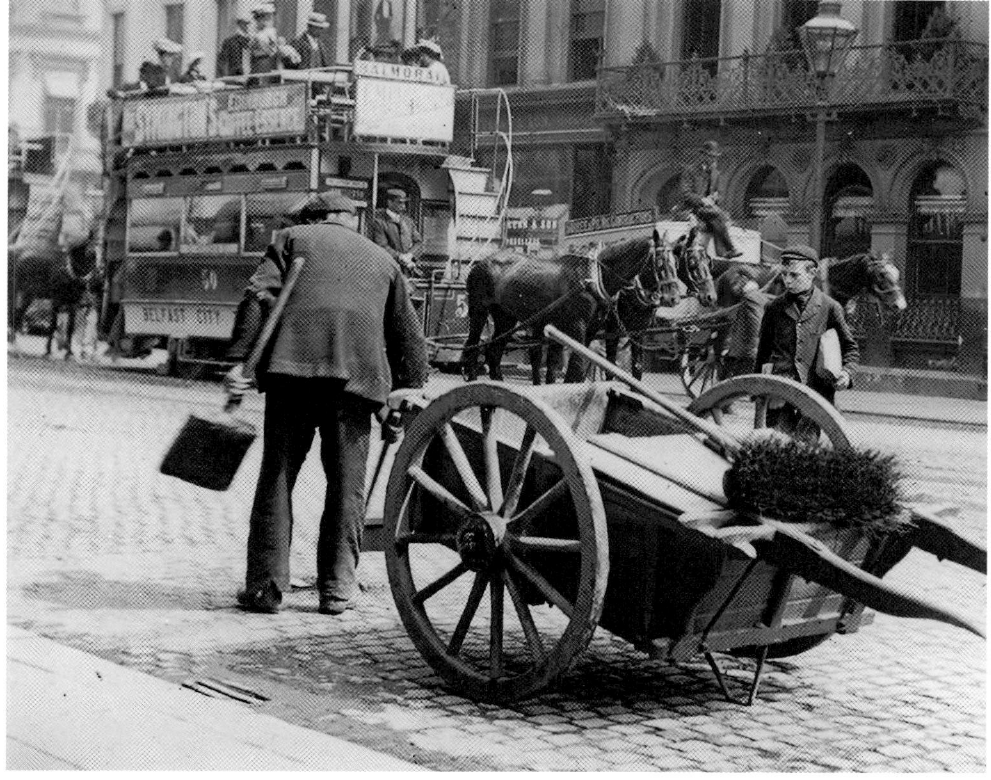

The horse drawn tramway service to the first Balmoral Show was well-patronised. This photograph from the Hogg Collection shows a "Balmoral" tram waiting in Donegall Place around 1902.
(Photograph: Courtesy Ulster Museum)

a liberal covering of litter, while lines of planks made the more quaggy places passable.

All departments of the Show came in for critical inspection from the big crowd of visitors, and, though there were some shakes of the head over the sheep and swine, the general verdict upon the exhibition was decidedly favourable. As for the grounds, notwithstanding that they were seen at a great disadvantage, owing to the "poaching" the surface had received during the last few days, their character, extent, and equipment were the subject of pleased surprise from every visitor new to the place. Up to twelve o'clock the parades of prize horses and cattle in the rings were watched with interest, but subsequently the displays on the trotting track drew all eyes on the jumping enclosure.

At half-past one the jumping competitions were resumed before a gathering which almost filled the available space, the crowd in the shilling part of the Ground being remarkably fine. The entertainment in the jumping-ground continued until half-past four, by which time the showyard proper was rapidly clearing, and by six o'clock the exhibition of 1896 was a thing of the past. The official returns of those who passed the turnstiles yesterday is 9,827. About 5,000 more were ticket-holders, making a total of nearly 15,000 visitors to the Showground.

This selection of Membership Tickets and Badges shows the diversity of shapes, sizes and colours used over the years. Of particular interest is the Lady Associate's Ticket of 1900 which was issued to Miss Edith Nugent, and the member's Ticket of 1902 in the name of J Milne Barbour who, in 1923, became President of the Society. He held this position, except for a brief period in the early Thirties, until 1951.

The following letter was received last night by Mr John Robson, Hon Secretary of the Association. It speaks for itself:- "Grand Central Hotel, 19 June 1896 – Dear Mr Robson, I congratulate the North-East Agricultural Society on the great success of their first Show in their splendid Showgrounds at Balmoral. Their plucky enterprise deserves every support. Will you kindly convey to the Council my wish to present a fifty-guinea challenge cup for competition in the harness section at their next Show. Thanking you and your Committee for their great courtesy – Faithfully yours, Thos Talbert Power."

The *Irish News* of the same date concurred with its morning rival *The Whig*:

The North-East Agricultural Association Show was brought to a close yesterday, when the attendance was something enormous, over ten thousand persons having paid for admission at the turnstiles. After such a record "gate" as this, there need be no fear that the Association will hesitate about making the arrangements for their next Show of the completest character, so that there will be no excuse for grumbling. Indeed, there was not much fault-finding in connection with the inaugural display at Balmoral, as everyone seemed to recognise the immense amount of work got through in the short time that has elapsed since the ground came into the Society's possession.

The unfavourable weather, no doubt, rendered things a bit uncomfortable; but on the whole the Show proved a decided success, and reflected the highest credit on the efforts of those who were primarily responsible for the change. In this connection, we must mention the names of Major Sharman Crawford, Mr Robson, Mr Gregg, and Mr Hugh C Kelly, the Secretary, all of whom were untiring in promoting the success of the undertaking, whilst the major portion of the clerical work incidental to the Show was capably performed by Mr Nicholl.

Yesterday proved much more enjoyable than either Thursday or Wednesday, as we were about winding up before the rain made its appearance, and the downpour was not nearly so copious as that of the previous afternoon. The Show did not suffer much by the rain, and the little that was lost to the coffers of the Association will be amply compensated for by the benefit which will accrue to the growing crops, and consequently to the agricultural community.

> The exhibition of a working dairy was one of the attractions of the Show yesterday, and those who inspected the cattle section were much interested in a Zulu bull and cow, the property of Mr Arthur Hamill, JP, which were on exhibition. The parade of the prize winners in the enclosure, the tandem driving, and trotting displays were all well appreciated, but undoubtedly the chief item of interest was the jumping, which was witnessed by an immense crowd.
>
> The Grand Stand enclosure was not so well filled as on Thursday, but the lower-priced portion, at the other side of the track, was packed. As on the previous day the band of the Royal Irish Constabulary from the Phoenix Park Depot, Dublin, discoursed a choice musical programme, under the conductorship of Mr Van Maanen. The train and tram services were most efficient, and an hour after the jumping had concluded at least four-fifths of the huge crowd had returned to the city. There were plenty of cars in evidence, and these were also well-patronised.

Given such glowing Press and public reaction, the confidence of the Association was such that in 1897 the Council decided to hold two Shows a year – one in Spring for draught horses, cattle, swine, poultry, dairy produce, implements, and machinery, and the other in Summer for light horses and sheep. The organisers noted ". . . it is gratifying to state that this departure has been attended by most encouraging results."[2]

In 1899, the Chief Secretary for Ireland Mr Gerald Balfour introduced a Bill for the establishment of a Department of Agriculture and other Industries and Technical Instruction in Ireland. The Council of the Association, together with the Chambers of Commerce in Dublin and Belfast and many other agricultural and commercial associations throughout Ireland had previously met Mr Balfour in Dublin. It was a complicated Bill, and the Council of the Association in conjunction with the Belfast Chamber of Commerce asked the Chief Secretary to come to Belfast in January 1900 to explain at length the provisions of the Act – an invitation which he readily accepted. It was clear that the Association was maintaining its reputation as a progressive organisation which was taken seriously by the Agricultural policy-makers of the day.

As the Association moved into the new century it struck a confident note.

> "It is nearly half a century since the Association came into active operation. At its formation there was but little expectation that it would assume the dimensions to which it has expanded, and in now taking a survey of the past, the members have every reason to be gratified at the enlarged field of usefulness to which it has extended its labours, and the singular success that has marked its career."[3] By 31 December 1900, the total membership was 860 and there were nearly 75 "Lady Associates", who were first introduced in 1899. However, the Association found itself in debt early in the new century – a reflection on the expenditure it had incurred in equipping its Balmoral premises"

In 1901 the then Secretary, Mr Kenneth MacRae estimated that the Association had spent "a sum upwards of £28,000" in "putting . . . the grounds – into proper order and erecting buildings and stands"[4] In the Annual Report for 1902 the Secretary Mr MacRae stated that a debt of £13,000 was hanging around their necks "like a millstone" and that the interest "was slowly strangling them to death". Unless that interest could be removed "the present year would be a serious one and would constitute the worst crisis in the history of the Association". It was decided to approach the Department of Agriculture and Technical Instruction in Dublin to ask that if the Association raised £6,500, would the Department give them pound for pound.

Colonel Sharman Crawford, a leading figure in the Association and a colourful character in the later history of Ulster, was reported to have spoken feelingly on this question of debt. According to the Report he believed that "if the Department did not help them, then the outlook was a serious one. The Department had used them to their own ends and without them, they would have no chance in carrying out their plans in the North of Ireland. He believed that Heaven helped those who helped themselves, and they were prepared to raise half the sum if they got pound for pound." His speech was greeted with "a great round of applause", and the motion to approach the Department was seconded by Lord Dunleath and adopted unanimously.

Edward VII and Queen Alexandra visited Balmoral on Monday 27th July 1903. Prior to their visit they unveiled a statue of Queen Victoria in front of the partially-built Belfast City Hall. (Photograph from Hogg Collection, Ulster Museum)

In the event, the Department did grant £6,500 to the Association, which itself raised another £10,233 - so the debt was more than cleared. The Annual Report of 1902 was accordingly upbeat and noted, in the quaint style of the times, that "members generally will share its satisfaction in the knowledge that the Society has overcome all pecuniary inconvenience, has assumed a broader sphere of usefulness and at present flourishes with still greater vigour and activity than before."

In July 1903 King Edward VII, with Queen Alexandra, visited Balmoral. They were received by the Marquis of Londonderry, the Lord Mayor Sir Daniel Dixon and Colonel Sharman Crawford. Mr Kenneth MacRae, Secretary of the Association, stated: "May it please your Majesty, we the members of the NE Agricultural Association regard the present advent of your gracious Majesty to Ireland and especially your visit to its commercial capital with unfeigned delight. It presents to your devoted historically loyal subjects of the North an opportunity to record their faithful and continued allegiance to the Throne and to symbolise by joy and gladness their gratitude and appreciation of his Majesty's unfailing sympathy and the welfare of this country."

The King's reply was short, but according to the *Belfast Newsletter*, "When he finished he was given the biggest outburst of cheering and applause ever heard in Belfast."

The King replied: "My lords and gentlemen, I am touched by your warm welcome and by the loyal and dutiful expression of your allegiance to my Throne and person. I have the fullest sympathy with your efforts to promote and foster an industry of such paramount importance in Ireland as agriculture. It gives me great pleasure to be able on the occasion of your Spring Show to contribute in however small a degree to its success."

The King and Queen apparently enjoyed the Balmoral Show and watched a parade of prize horses, and also a horse jumping competition. Before leaving, the King expressed his appreciation of the reception which had been given to their Majesties and "greatly referred to the pleasure it had afforded them to be present."

The Royal couple had already spent several days in the South of Ireland where they visited, among other places, Maynooth College. They arrived in Newtownards Station from Dublin on Saturday 25 July, and spent the weekend at Mount Stewart as guests of the Marquis and Marchioness of Londonderry. On Monday 27 July they unveiled a Statue of Queen Victoria at Belfast City Hall, and later visited the Royal Victoria Hospital where the Queen named a new ward. They arrived at Balmoral at 3.30 pm, and left at 4.20 pm for Bangor where they boarded the Royal Yacht and set sail for Lough Swilly. They then visited, in turn, Buncrana, Galway, Berehaven and Cork before leaving for Cowes. Clearly Royal visits to Ireland in those days were as much a test of stamina as of diplomacy.

The Royal visit coincided with another historic development. The Association called a special meeting on 20 May 1903 to alter its rules and to change the name to the Ulster Agricultural Society, with new offices at 7 Donegall Square West. Among other measures it was agreed that the number of elected members of Council be reduced from 96 to 72, and that five members be appointed annually by the Department of Agriculture and Technical Instruction for Ireland.

It is not recorded as to whether or not the significant change in name was a reflection on the current feeling of a distinct Ulster identity as the long-running Home Rule crisis began to reach its height, but the strong determination of the Province to keep the link with Britain was symbolised by a petition in 1904 from the Association to seek permission to use the prefix "Royal". A letter from Dublin indicated that this wish had been granted.

Dublin Castle
28 January 1904

Sir,

With ref. to your letter of the 12th inst. on the subject of the petition of the UAS asking for permission to use the prefix "Royal" in the name of the Society I am directed by the Lord Lieutenant to state that the petition, having been laid before the King, His Majesty has been graciously pleased to approve of the desired permission being granted and the command of the Society be known as the Royal Ulster Agricultural Society.

signed
JB Dougherty

It was no surprise that the Minutes of Council for 1 January 1904 had noted the Chairman as saying that they were beginning the new year with a new name, new rules, new offices and with a clean balance sheet. He hoped that "Such a thing as an overdraft . . . would never be mentioned in connection with the Society again . . . " His hopes that they would be favoured "in a very short time" with the prefix "Royal" were indeed fulfilled, before the end of the month.

After such heady excitement, it was interesting to note that, in the way of such things, the Annual Report for 1905 stated that "nothing of importance has happened in the working of the Society for the past twelve months to call for special comment."

The years leading to the First World War, though momentous in the history of Ulster and Ireland as the Home Rule Crisis deepened, were comparatively quiet in the history of the RUAS. The Report for 1908 recorded that the Society had 1,006 members – a sizeable increase from 860 in the year 1900. By 31 December 1908 there were 286 Life Members, 630 Annual Members and 90 Lady Associates.

The weather, as ever, was unpredictable. The Annual Report for 1904 noted a big drop in Show takings due to bad weather. Colonel Sharman Crawford stated that "of course they had money in the bank, they were still on the right side of the account, but unless they had better weather in the future, they did not know what might occur. During the time Mr MacRae had been Secretary, fifteen out of sixteen Shows were visited by rain, the weather at the last two

Shows being the worst since they went to Balmoral." Even worse was to come. A Report in the *Belfast Telegraph* of 18 February 1910 stated:

> The hurricane on Thursday was responsible for serious damage at the Balmoral Showgrounds Belfast where the extensive building known as the Londonderry Hall was blown down. Two apprentice painters who were at work at the time inside were warned by the trembling of the structures and got clear in the nick of time. The hall which will be rebuilt at once was the finest in the grounds, being 200 yards long and cattle and horses were stalled in it at Show time.

A disaster of a different kind occurred at Balmoral more than two years later when an airman was killed during an exhibition of flying. This was thought to be the first aviation accident in Ireland, and the *Belfast Newsletter* had a full account in its edition of 23 September 1912. The very detailed reporting, replete with purple prose, is a contrast to the crisper style of today's media, but it nevertheless graphically conveys a great sense of drama.

8 BELFAST EV

FIRST AVIATION FATALITY IN IRELAND

ASTLEY KILLED AT BELFAST.

THE WRECKED MONOPLANE.

INSET SHOWS THE LATE MR. ASTLEY (RIGHT), WITH MR. VALENTINE AND MONS. SALMET (CENTRE).

The air disaster at Balmoral in September 1912 when aviator H J D Astley was killed. The photograph, published in the then *Belfast Evening Telegraph*, shows the wrecked monoplane with the late Mr Astley on the extreme right in the inset.

The Bleriot Monoplane in which Mr Astley met his death photographed in the Arena before the crash.

A shocking fatality occurred on Saturday last at the Balmoral Showgrounds, where an exhibition of flying was being given by Mr HJD Astley and Mr James Valentine, both of whom, it will be remembered, took part in the Dublin to Belfast race, and subsequently, on behalf of local charities, gave an interesting display at the grounds belonging to the Royal Ulster Agricultural Society. This was the second occasion on which the two aviators had appeared together at Balmoral. On Saturday the conditions appeared to be altogether favourable, and about half-past three a very successful flight was made by Mr Valentine. His colleague came out shortly afterwards, and his Bleriot monoplane made a beautiful ascent.

An aeronaut of extraordinary skill and daring, Mr Astley flew around in a wide circle, and so far as could be seen, his machine was acting splendidly. He rose to a considerable altitude at one time, but subsequently he "dipped" closer to the east, and, to the admiration of the spectators, caused his machine to scud across the enclosure with all the grace and swiftness of a bird. Suddenly the admiration was changed to alarm. Mr Astley, after flying to the northern end of the aerodrome, near the starting point, was seen to be canting his machine over in order to make a sharp turn. It was then that the danger came, and although the majority of the spectators did not detect it, Mr Valentine and others who were familiar with the science and practice of aviation realised it only too well. For a moment the machine appeared to become stationary as it turned vertically, head to wind. Immediately underneath a number of spectators were assembled, and the pilot, realising that the aeroplane was side-slipping, and that a fall was inevitable, kept turning inwards to the left with the object of riding clear of the ground. He succeeded in this, but he was unable to avert the awful peril by which he himself was confronted. At the low altitude at which the machine was moving it was impossible to right it, and a cry of horror went up as it crashed to the ground with terrible force.

> Everybody realised that there had been a dreadful accident, but it was hoped that the aviator had at least escaped with his life. Several medical men happened to be on the ground, and they ran over to the enclosure, where the unfortunate pilot was lying amongst the wreckage of his machine. Others also tried to gain admission, but they were kept back by a strong force of police, acting under District-Inspector Redmond. Several ladies actively interested in aviation were in the enclosure, and they showed the utmost sympathy and solicitude for the injured man, one of them taking off a long coat which she was wearing in order that he might be placed upon it. Amongst the spectators the accident caused a feeling of awe and consternation, and many women fainted as a result of the shock.

Despite the frantic work of doctors and other staff, Astley died of a "fractured skull and brain lacerations." Others were more fortunate. According to the newspapers: "One of the spectators, a stout man in an overcoat, came very near to his end. One of the wings of the machine touched him slightly and sent him reeling to the side of the railings." Unfortunately it was not Mr Astley's first accident. He had earlier crashed into a stone wall at a flying display in Wales, and he also crashed on a flight from Liege to London, accompanied by a Miss Trehawke Davies. Mr Astley, when his aircraft struck the ground on that occasion and "half buried itself in the earth" was astonished to find himself alive. But he added "When I got up, there was Miss Davies fixing her camera. 'Dear me' she said 'what a pity – we shall just have to go back by train.' She could not have been cooler if she had stepped out of a cab." The early flyers were true pioneers.

The First World War from 1914-18 led to a suspension of Shows at Balmoral which was used as a Remount Depot by the military authorities. Extreme difficulty was experienced in agreeing on acceptable financial arrangement for the utilisation of the Showgrounds by the War Office and when negotiations broke down, application was made to the Defence of the Realm Losses Commission. That action, however, did not bring the expected solution and the obvious anger of the Finance Committee was expressed in their response to the findings of the Commission. – "The Society has received your letter of 28 May 1915 and notes with astonishment the decision at which the Commission has arrived, that decision the Society absolutely declines to accept". Many more months elapsed before final settlement was reached. Even after the War, there were continuing problems and the grounds were still accommodating 600 artillery horses - due to the sectarian troubles in Belfast. Strangely, while the War itself caused untold death and suffering across Europe, the records of the Society – like those of other institutions in Ireland – were businesslike, and even mundane. The Annual Report for 1914, for example, reported an outbreak of Foot and Mouth Disease, and also recorded the death of the President Lord Londonderry.

On 19 May 1915, the Society presented an Address to Lord Wimbourne, the Lord Lieutenant, in the name of Colonel Sharman Crawford, the President, and Kenneth MacRae, the Secretary. The respectful and convoluted style of the Address, and the reply, is scarcely believable in this more abrasive age. Members of the Society . . . tender to you a cordial and respectful welcome on your advent to Ireland and to reiterate our unwavering and determined loyalty and attachment to the Throne and constitution of His Most Gracious Majesty, King George.

> How much he could have wished that your esteemed visit to Belfast had synchronised with a time of peace and not one of sadness when grim visaged war fraught with all the fiendish ingenuity that an unscrupulous foe can contemplate and impose, when poor humanity pales at premeditated acts of barbarity, when deliberate and medieval savagery in violation of every international obligation is cynically exercised to intimidate and overawe and when vandalism ruthlessly practised lays waste for ever the intrinsic and monumental treasures of ages ancient and august . . .
>
> It would be idle to pretend that we are not heartily proud of the spontaneous response given by vigorous sons of our colonies and by the flower of our manhood at home to the call of our Sovereign in times of need and we especially rejoice that when rallying to the colours in firm allegiance the men of Ulster play no laggards part . . . Our heartiest greeting we pleasurably give to your Excellency and to Lady Wimborne this day for the joint honour you have accorded to our city, and we earnestly pray that your Excellency's tenure of office may be marked by an infinitable measure of happiness and prosperity. . .

Lord Wimborne replied:

> I come among you as the representative of our Royal Master, King George, and that fact alone would have guaranteed me a respectful welcome at the hands of the community whose loyalty to the Throne and devotion to the Empire had ever been manifest. But there rings in your words a note of personal kindliness to Lady Wimborne and myself which we are as yet only entitled by anticipation and which indicates a spirit of generosity on your part of which we shall always be conscious on discharging the important and onerous duties which it falls to our lot to fulfil.
>
> For nine terrible months we and our allies have confronted the ambitions of a prepared and determined aggressor and the end is not yet. The land he has ravished still remains in foul embrace. Though his ships cannot ride the sea there ever lurks beneath its surface the instruments of his powered hate and murderous design against defenceless non-combatants. The sacrifices in life and treasure that have been made by these islands have been many and sore, yet we cannot close our eyes to the fact that still greater efforts and losses are before us, but we shall go forward with sober resolve, fighting in a righteous cause until it triumphs in a peace, free from frightful menace and secured for ourselves and those who come after us. When that happy day arrives, Belfast, continuing steadfastly in the way she is going, will be able to look back in satisfaction on the part she played in the struggle. This city with the Counties Down and Antrim have already since the outbreak of war sent to the colours

> two of every nine of the men of military age, this apart from the men on His Majesty's ships who are guarding us from the horrors of invasion. Neither does it include those rendering regular, steady and invaluable services in shipyards, ropeworks, foundries and other establishments . . .

The speech continued 'ad infinitum' but behind the flowery language lay a stark reality. By the end of the First World War, some 49,000 Irishmen including a total of 24,000 from Armagh, Down, Antrim, Londonderry, Tyrone and Fermanagh, had lost their lives, and many thousands of others had been wounded. Despite such horrors, the War brought considerable economic prosperity to the whole of Ireland, North and South. David Johnson, the historian, notes: "The cause of this upsurge in activity was simply that the War effort made heavy demands on those goods which had traditionally been produced within the Province, namely textiles, foodstuffs and shipping."[5]

There was an increased demand for linen goods for military purposes, including tents, haversacks, and hospital equipment, and the acreage under flax within Ireland was doubled. War brought unprecedented affluence to agriculture. With traditional sea-routes rendered hazardous by German U-boats, the United Kingdom, including all of Ireland, had to rely on local producers. By 1917 for example British and Irish farmers were supplying 90 per cent of beef compared to 60 per cent before the War.

> The result was that Ulster's farmers, like those in the rest of the Country, were operating in a seller's market. Agriculture in Ireland generally prospered even more than in Britain as governmental attempts to control prices were less successful in the former, largely because of the numerical strength of the farming community and their general resistance to state intervention.[6]

After the war ended, the high level of economic activity in the Province continued, with buoyant demand in linen and shipbuilding. The price of agricultural commodities kept pace with the cost of living, and the *Northern Whig* in its review of 1919 noted that "the price of land had soared to a remarkable degree." But the economic good times did not last. As David Johnson notes: "For farmers the income levels achieved in 1919 – 20 were not regained for over a decade and not markedly surpassed until the Second World War."[7]

The map of Ireland was changing, partly for reasons so graphically outlined by Winston Churchill, in 1922:

> Then came the Great War. Every institution in the world was strained. Great empires have been overturned. The whole map of Europe has been changed. The positions of countries have been violently altered. The modes of thought of men, the whole outlook on affairs, the grouping of parties all have encountered violent and tremendous change in the deluge that has swept the world. But as the deluge subsides and the waters fall short, we see the dreary steeples of Fermanagh and Tyrone emerging once again. The integrity of their quarrel is one of the few institutions that has been unaltered in the cataclysm that has swept the world.

The Government of Ireland Act of 1920 attempted to solve the problem posed by the integrity of that long and bitter Irish quarrel by creating two parliaments – one in Dublin and one in Belfast. The nationalist Cahir Healy, as Chairman of the Enniskillen Poor Law Guardians, made one last plea:

> The Belfast Parliament will be a parliament of Planters, with half of Ulster outside or ignoring its decrees. We offer to our fellow-countrymen in Ulster in the Parliament of Ireland every guarantee that can make them secure, religiously and commercially. Frankly, we need their help and they need ours. Ulster farmers have everything to gain by standing by us in a United Ireland. The religious difficulty has been solved in Switzerland, in Germany and elsewhere. Surely to God, we in Ireland can live in peace.

With the benefit of hindsight, his words – like his hopes for peace – some 70 years ago, seem so poignant today. The partition of Ireland posed its own challenges, problems and aspirations for the people of this island and not least for those engaged in agriculture. The world which had witnessed the formation of the old North-East Agricultural Association of Ireland in 1854 had changed beyond recognition.

NOTES

1 The North-East Agricultural Association
– extract from Ireland, Industrial and Agricultural 1901, p.123
2 Ibid op.cit p.125
3 Ibid op.cit p.126
4 Ibid op.cit p.123
5 An Economic History of Ulster 1820-1939 Edited by Liam Kennedy and Philip Ollerenshaw
and published by Manchester University Press p.184
6 op.cit p.185
7 op.cit p.188

The late John McRobert of Crossgar was a well known breeder of Clydesdale horses in the 1920's. This photograph shows one of his many champions "Rademon Sunshine" at the 1921 Balmoral Show.

ALL THE KING'S MEN . . . AND WOMEN *Chapter 3*

BETWEEN THE FIRST AND SECOND WORLD WARS, Northern Ireland's three major areas of employment – shipbuilding, linen and agriculture – were "adversely affected by world-wide economic developments which, to a large extent, local industrialists, farmers and Government Ministers were powerless to control."[1] In 1926, agriculture employed a third of the male and a quarter of the total labour force in Northern Ireland. Compared to industrial goods, the prices of agricultural products decreased in the Twenties and there was a significant fall in 1929-30. Holdings were small and output per head was low, with the local level only 46 per cent of the British output in 1924. To have changed farming speedily by consolidating holdings would have been socially difficult. As David Johnson notes memorably:

> It was, in any case, politically impossible, such was the strength of the agricultural lobby in the Northern Ireland Parliament. As one disgruntled Belfast MP noted: "If a farmer wanted somebody to blow his nose, some Hon Member would get up and raise the question . . . and a man would be appointed not only to blow the farmer's nose, but to wipe it for him."[2]

Having been advised by Lord Clanwilliam of the formation in 1826 of the North East Society (see Chapter 1), it is possible that this was a souvenir of the Centenary Celebrations. The fact that no reference is made to the Centenary suggests that the Office Bearers of the day were not entirely convinced that the North East Society had any connection with the RUAS.

The purchase in 1931 of seven acres, running alongside Harberton Park, provided much-needed additional space for parking. The Harberton Park of the 1930's, with its wide open spaces, looks very different to that of the 1990's.

David Johnson further notes that although agriculture in Northern Ireland improved between the wars compared to Britain, in absolute terms it remained far behind:

> Although the inter-war period saw considerable progress, the Province's agricultural community remained miserably poor both in comparison with Britain, and with the industrial sector in Northern Ireland. The living standards of farmers with less than thirty acres were in most cases below those of industrial wage earners, while the income of farm labourers, 25s to 27s 6d per week in the 1930's, was less than the 30s benefit paid to an unemployed married man. This was to create considerable problems after 1936 when agriculture was brought within the scope of the insurance acts, as farm labourers were frequently better off out of work than in.[3]

Given the underlying economic difficulties between the wars, Northern Ireland generally slipped behind the United Kingdom. Johnson further notes that "in many respects its performance was quite comparable to other regions of Britain which had also been adversely affected by declining markets for their products" including the North East, Scotland and Wales. He also stresses, however, that progress did take place.

> Incomes rose, housing improved, mortality fell, social life became more varied. In short, despite all the Province's economic problems, the conditions of life for the vast majority of the Ulster people were better in 1939 than they had been 20 years before.[4]

Against such a general background, the Royal Ulster Agricultural Society progressed steadily in size, scope and membership and in doing so it not only took account of, but also tried to ameliorate, some of the hardship of the existing social conditions.

One of the main priorities by the late Twenties was a membership drive. In 1929 there were about 1,100 Annual Members on the register at £1 each, and 155 Life Members. Income from subscriptions was £1,085:13:0, but the Register needed revising. In 1931 a drive for new Members was started, and aided later by the publication of a journal *The Balmoral Bulletin*, it was entirely successful. The journal was self-supporting by advertising, and each month's issue contained the names of candidates for Membership, with the names of their proposers. This acted as a spur in increasing the Membership, and by the end of 1933 almost 3,000 new Members had been secured.

By May 1935, the target of 5,000 Members was in sight, and the publication of *The Balmoral Bulletin* then ceased, as the growing burden of work was becoming too heavy for the small Secretarial staff of four. In addition, there was a growing outcry from Members about the shortage of seats in the Jumping Enclosure – this in spite of the fact that in 1920, a second Grand Stand (the North Stand), was built. This reinforced concrete structure seating 700 was designed by Thomas W Henry. A third Grand Stand (the South Stand), accommodating 1,600 people, was added in 1932. This imposing structure, designed by Archibald Leitch, was formally opened during the Annual Show by the Prime Minister of Northern Ireland who received a beautiful silver inkstand as a memento of the occasion. The Society, of course, had to sell all these seats at each Show, to set the income against the outlay. The South Stand, incidentally, cost £4,000 and brought the total covered seating to 2,700. To satisfy the requirement for a substantial indoor facility for exhibitions, the Central Exhibition Hall was erected in 1926 at a cost of £6,000. The Ministry of Agriculture generously contributed one third of the cost and subsequently paid a further £1,500 to enable an annex to be built to accommodate livestock as part of their educational exhibit at Balmoral Show. To this day the Ministry and their successor the Department of Agriculture have used this Hall to promote the industry at successive Balmoral Shows. The Central Exhibition Hall was extensively refurbished in 1995 and was renamed The Balmoral Hall.

The idea of communicating with members through the *Balmoral Bulletin* was much appreciated, and the magazine kept everyone in touch about what was happening at the Royal Ulster. The modern day equivalent is the three times a year, *Balmoral News*.

One matter worth mentioning is how Northern Ireland pig breeders gained entry for their stock in the National Pig Breeders' Association Herd Book. When Sam Clarke took up his duties at Balmoral as Secretary Manager, he was responsible for compiling the Large White Ulster Pig Herd Book, the first volume of which was published in 1909.

In 1933 Sam Clarke was approached by a number of leading breeders with a request to start a Herd Book for Large White York Pigs. He discussed the matter with the Secretary of the National Pig Breeders' Association and told them that the long, lean type of pig, known as the "Large White York", which had been bred very successfully in Ulster for many years, would probably be suitable for registration in the NPBA Herd Book. (It had been closed for 15 years to all pigs born outside Great Britain.)

A classic example of a high-quality Large White pig is expertly examined (at a safe distance!) at the 1947 Annual Show. The pig Gostrode King David 5th, exhibited and shown by James Pollock & Sons, was Supreme Pig Champion in both 1947 and 1948.

Eventually, an Inspection Committee of English breeders was set up. They visited Ulster herds and this resulted in the opening of the NPBA Herd Book to leading herds in Northern Ireland. The Royal Ulster Pig Committee was naturally very pleased with the outcome, which opened a market hitherto closed to Ulster breeders, and also enabled them to introduce new blood strains.

The attendance at the Shows was growing rapidly. In 1931 the Society took an option on leasing (from Viscount Harberton) seven acres of ground bounding the Showgrounds at Harberton Park, to provide parking for 1,000 cars and additional space for Trade Exhibits. The rent was £350 per year. Hitherto, horse-boxes and lorries had used Balmoral Avenue or the Lisburn Road and had caused considerable traffic jams. By 1932, some 97,974 people attended the Show, a United Kingdom record, and by 1933 this had risen to 105,602. The Society's Annual Report for 1933 listed the continued improvements at Balmoral, including new equipment in the jumping enclosure, new ticket offices, and drainage. In May of that year the Duke of Abercorn, as Patron of the Society, inaugurated a new Exhibition Hall in the presence of a distinguished gathering by turning the first turf on the site of the new building. It was to become The King's Hall which was opened in 1934 and marked a milestone in the history of the Society.

In 1932 and 1933 Sam Clarke had unofficial talks with the architect Archibald Leitch about a large Exhibition Hall, with a frontage on the Lisburn Road. Leitch drew up plans for a building some 300 feet long by 152 feet wide. The Government agreed to a loan of £60,000, under the Public Loans Utility Act, at 4 1/8 per cent over 30 years. Subsequently, the Government agreed that £10,000 of the loan should rank as a grant, in view of the fact that the building work would provide much-needed employment for many ex-Servicemen, some of whom had been out of work for several years.

News of the imaginative new project to be built by local contractors J and R Thompson of Roden Street, Belfast (using the Considère system) was announced to the Press on 24 February 1933, with a strict embargo "until after 11.30 am . . . the time and date fixed for the Society's Annual Meeting". The Press Release was headed "Work for Unemployed", and given the grand design of the project, it was written with not a little awe and some pride:

> In taking this momentous step, the Society will have rendered an invaluable service to the great Agricultural Industry of Northern Ireland, for which is has laboured zealously for so many years. At the same time, it will have afforded to all manufacturing concerns in a highly industrialised centre the means of establishing direct contact with potential users of their goods.

The new Exhibition Hall will be of most imposing appearance and will have its main frontage to the Lisburn Road, from which there will be a curved carriage way to the main entrance. The building will be constructed in reinforced concrete under the most modern system, and will have a span on the arch principle of 152 feet. The length of the Hall will be 300 feet, and the height from the ground floor to the apex of the roof will be 64 feet.

Prior to the building of The King's Hall in 1934, this was the imposing entrance which greeted visitors to Balmoral!

The Main Entrance will be terraced, and the massive columns rising from the frontage line will add tremendously to the appearance of the building, which will be a most impressive landmark, situated, as it will be, on what is now one of the busiest roads in the United Kingdom, and the main artery between Northern and Southern Ireland.

The Administrative Block of offices, comprising the Secretary's Office and General Offices, will be situated to the left of the Main Entrance. On the right, provision has been made for a Post Office, Public Telephones, Cloak Rooms, and Waiting Rooms, all of ample dimensions. At the other end of the Hall, restaurants and kitchens will be provided; also a platform for public events,

The construction of The King's Hall was a major feat of engineering. The "shape" of the new building can just be discerned through the tangled web of scaffolding.

with suitable retiring rooms. Full provision has been made for stands for exhibition purposes on the Ground Floor, with power and lighting facilities for each separate unit. The Stands generally will be uniform in type, and will be portable, so that the Ground Floor of the Hall can be cleared to render it suitable for the holding of functions of various kinds.

The Balcony Floor, which will be approached by four staircases, will have a Council Chamber, General Committee Room, Members' Library, and Writing Room. The partitions dividing these rooms will be portable, thus rendering the rooms available for use for concerts on a small scale, and other gatherings for which the Main Hall would be too large. The Balcony will run the whole length of the Hall on both sides and at the ends, and, being 20 feet in width at the sides, will provide further accommodation for exhibition purposes. Stands 10 to 12 feet in depth will be erected there.

Lighting during the day time will be obtained from vertical lantern lights, running the whole length of the stepped roof, and these lights, being provided with controlled glazed openings, will ensure that the building will be thoroughly ventilated. Additional lighting will be obtained from the front and back gables, both of which will be glazed. Electric lighting of the most modern type, including a flood lighting system, will be installed, and particular attention will be paid to exhibitors' requirements in connection with the lighting of their stands.

The building will be steam heated, provision having been made for the heating of the Administrative Block and large Hall to be operated independently. The main structure will be fireproof, and special attention has been given to the provision of an adequate number of exits, situated at the most convenient points. The whole building, when seating has been provided, will be capable of accommodating 8,000 people.

It will thus be seen that this great Hall, which will be one of the largest and most complete of its kind in the United Kingdom, will be eminently suitable for exhibitions of all kinds, thus meeting a need which has become most pressing in our highly industrialised Province, where exhibition space of a suitable nature has not been available hitherto. If one can visualise the vast proportions of the building and its lay-out, it will be realised that the uses to which it can be put will be endless. Northern Ireland has never yet attempted to run a Motor Show on a large scale, for the simple reason that there has been no building capable of staging such a Show to advantage. The local motor trade, therefore, will be placed in a position to make a display of the various makes of cars on a scale worthy of its importance. In addition to Trade Exhibitions of all kinds, the Hall will be capable of housing carnivals, such as are provided annually for the entertainment of the Glasgow public in Kelvin Hall, circuses, boxing matches, bazaars, fetes, and all kinds of public gatherings. In fact it will be the "Olympia" of Ulster.

A major internal feature of The King's Hall is the series of portals at 25ft intervals along the length of the building. This photograph of the construction of the portals indicates the use of a considerable number of $1^{1}/_{2}$" diameter steel reinforcing rods and emphasises the important role they play in providing stability for the building.

The installation of the telephone switchboard in the new offices at The King's Hall is closely supervised by Secretary/Manager Sam Clarke (right).

Despite the concerns expressed that The King's Hall would not be ready for the official opening on 29th May 1934, such fears proved unfounded. It should be noted that the word "Agricultural" does not appear in the title – there was not enough room!

> The action of the Society in embarking on this enterprise, at a time when employment is urgently needed, will be approved by the whole community. Indeed, the prevailing need for work at the present time has weighed largely with the Society in undertaking this great scheme, which would not have been entered upon for some time to come save in exceptional circumstances.

The Architect, from London, had been consulted early on, and the Royal Society of Ulster Architects protested formally at the appointment of other than an Ulster firm of Architects. Work began in June 1933 and it was opened by His Royal Highness the Duke of Gloucester on 29 May 1934. By Order of King George V, the building was named 'The King's Hall'. Speaking at a luncheon afterwards, the Duke of Gloucester said: "I shall tell the King that the addition to these premises is in every way an appropriate structure to be named after His Majesty."

The Royal visitor also expressed astonishment on learning that the erection of the building had only begun on 15 June in the previous year, and that twelve days prior to opening, a great part

There was great excitement on 29th May 1934 when HRH The Duke of Gloucester visited Balmoral to open The King's Hall, the biggest project ever undertaken by the Society. In the photograph the Royal visitor is introduced to Members of the Council by the President Sir Milne Barbour (centre). The King's Hall quickly became a landmark of international renown, and its presence and features were suitably recognised by the Department of the Environment in April 1991 when it was placed on the list of buildings of special architectural and historic interest.

of the construction work on the balcony and staircase was incomplete, also there was no floor in the building – nor were the stands erected. There was no sign that a few weeks prior to the Royal visit it appeared to almost everyone that even a superhuman effort would not see everything in readiness – nevertheless well ordered plans were carried through and the result was a triumph for those responsible.

Simultaneously with the building of The King's Hall, provision was made for accommodation for working machinery exhibits at the Annual Shows, on a site at the immediate rear of the Hall. This took the form of covered shedding and open space, with gas, water and electricity being laid on. From its inception, space in that area was always at a premium.

However there was more to Balmoral than interest in the magnificent new King's Hall, and more to the Annual Show than met the eye – as the *Belfast Newsletter* noted in a Special Supplement to coincide with the Duke's visit:

> When the weather is fine Balmoral Show becomes a sort of Ulster "Ascot" as far as fashions are concerned, for the Show is popular with women and is always an occasion for smart frocks. On one of the days his Grace the Governor and the Duchess of Abercorn pay a semi-State visit. This is one of the big social events of the Ulster year, and might be said to attract the cream of the society of the Six Counties.

The statue of King George VI which was erected on the balcony of The King's Hall in 1937

There is one other aspect of the Show which is important. It causes a tremendous circulation of money with a consequent benefit to many classes of the community, and gives a fillip to all sorts of trades and professions. This year the visit of HRH the Duke of Gloucester is bound to be of enormous benefit to local industry, particularly to those engaged in making and supplying clothing of all kinds, for the various functions that have been arranged will be attended by many hundreds of people, men and women, who will want to look their smartest. On the occasion of a previous Royal visit – that of the Duke and Duchess of York – one Belfast millinery establishment sold £400 worth of women's hats in a week, and this was only a small part of the big trade that was done throughout the Province.

Returning to more basic matters, minor work continued on The King's Hall under the main contract until July 1935, and the Consultants' final statement of their account on 3 November 1937 amounted to £61,139:0s:8d – a sum commendably close to the original estimate. The Statue of King George VI which now adorns the main hall was created by the sculptor Sir William Reid Dick. It was the first sculpture made of the King and was commissioned by the *Daily Mail*. The Society bought it from the Newspaper Company after its "Ideal Homes" Exhibition in 1937. On completion, The King's Hall was the largest ferro concrete building in the British Isles, outside London where the Westminster Horticultural Hall, built in 1929 was the most nearly comparable building. It was, by current standards, a considerable building and engineering achievement. It provided over 66,500 square feet of exhibition space, and, at the time of its opening, it had seating accommodation for five times as many people as in any other building in Northern Ireland.

The material excavated from the site, over one month, was 2,530 tons, and a considerable amount of supplies were needed for the building. They included 4,500 tons of stones and screenings; 2,300 tons of sand; 1,200 tons of British Portland cement, 530 tons of steel bars; and 25,000 superficial yards of timber for casings. Eleven huge spans, each measuring 152 feet and resting on 22 enormous concrete blocks, were required in the construction of the Hall. On completion The King's Hall became not only a local landmark but also an important amenity for the agricultural, industrial, business, social and cultural life of Northern Ireland. In an age of symbolism it remains arguably the greatest single landmark of the work and role of the Royal Ulster Agricultural Society and of its standing in the local community and further afield.

The provision of machinery sheds at the rear of The King's Hall proved to be very popular for both exhibitors and visitors to Balmoral Shows. Unfortunately this facility had to be demolished to make way for the erection of the Nugent Hall.

The landmark of course has changed in appearance over the years occasioned by the necessity to re-roof the Hall in 1981/82. This enforced change whilst greatly improving the internal aesthetics and facilities did not however meet with the approval of everyone. Paul Larmour in his book "The Architectural Heritage of Malone and Stranmillis" (published by U.A.H.S.), noted that "the obscuring of the original roof and the negation of the roof lights' special function has spoiled a very important building".

The Society lost no time in making use of its splendid Exhibition Hall, and the Annual Report for 1936 noted that no fewer than 15 events were held in it. They included Exhibitions, Dog Shows, Evangelical Meetings, Boxing and Wrestling Contests, and a Christmas Circus. There was one major problem with the Hall, however. Due to the lack of suitable seating, the Society was losing valuable bookings. A special committee was authorised by the Council to appeal to each member to donate at least £1, the estimated cost of a single chair plus the contribution to a raised platform. Within a short time, the appeal had raised more than £700.

Over the years, the Society had to contend with considerable damage to its property due to severe weather, and other factors. As was noted earlier,[5] the Londonderry Hall was blown down in a hurricane in February 1910, the Royal Grand Stand was damaged by fierce gales in November 1928, and in March 1936, a blizzard wrecked the Harberton, Deramore and Downshire Halls. With the Annual Show only ten weeks away, all this accommodation had to be replaced. This was done in timber, and the heavy cost had to be met by the Society. Although the buildings were insured for about £15,000, the insurance companies refused to pay compensation, holding that the damage was an 'Act of God'.

Sartorial elegance has been one of the eye-catching features of the Show over the years. In this 1930's photograph the style of an entire family has been captured for posterity.

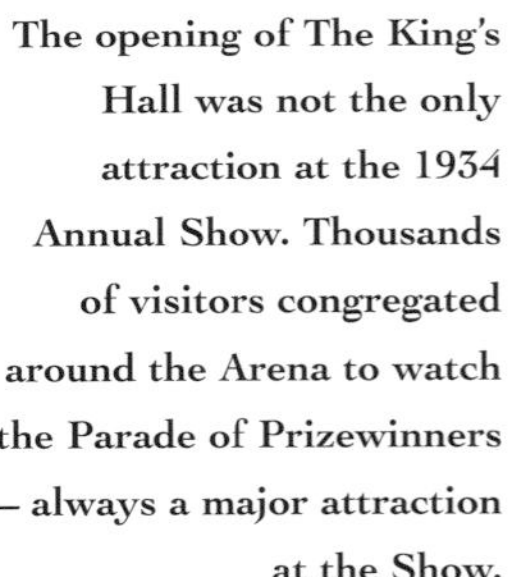

The opening of The King's Hall was not the only attraction at the 1934 Annual Show. Thousands of visitors congregated around the Arena to watch the Parade of Prizewinners – always a major attraction at the Show.

1937 was Coronation Year and although there was no Royal Visitor at the Annual Show, every effort was made to celebrate the occasion with flags and bunting decorating the Royal Stand. The large crowd at the Arena is fascinated by the appearance of Milestone, the Hackney Champion owned by the father of the Rev W J Watson, MBE, currently a member of Council.

To mark the Coronation of King George VI in 1937, the Society set out to highlight this noteworthy event by staging the best Show in its history. According to the Annual Report for 1937, the Show in May attracted nearly 100,000 people 'in perfect weather'. Later that year, on July 20, the Balmoral Showgrounds were chosen by the Government as the venue for the Uniformed Organisations of Ulster to meet King George and Queen Elizabeth on their Coronation visit to Belfast. Again 'in glorious weather' some 25,000 children from all parts of Ulster greeted their Majesties in the jumping enclosure, 'which was beautifully decorated.'

Despite such celebrations, the war-clouds were once again gathering across Europe. In the late Thirties the Society placed four of its buildings at the disposal of the Air Raid Precautions Committee of Belfast Corporation for the storage of gas masks. Thousands of volunteers attended the Showgrounds, and it was reckoned that more than half-a-million gas masks were assembled and packed into special boxes.

The Society's grounds and premises were occupied almost from the outbreak of the Second World War on September 3, 1939, until some months after hostilities ceased. In succession there were Anti-Aircraft Gunners, an Infantry Regiment (10th Worcesters) and Army lorry drivers in training. The RASC (1,650 strong) returned from Dunkirk after June 1940 and set up No.1 Base Supply Depot for troops in Northern Ireland. The latter were succeeded by the Air Ministry (Ministry of Supply), who converted all the main premises in the Showgrounds into an Aircraft Factory to build, for Short Bros & Harland, the chassis for Shorts–Stirling bombers – the first to drop 100 ton loads of bombs on Cologne, Hamburg and other key German targets. The factory ran day and night for some months after war ceased and continued making aircraft components.

An American Field Bakery Unit occupied the Jumping Enclosure and some covered accommodation, until the main body of American troops arrived in strength. There was training for British and American Servicemen, and it was estimated that the Units turned out between 30,000 – 40,000 lbs of bread daily for Army Camps in Northern Ireland. The Implements Shed at the rear of The Kings Hall was used to store Auxiliary Fire Service Appliances. For this privilege, The Lord Mayor, Aldermen and citizens of Belfast paid the Society the princely sum of one shilling annually! Despite the wholesale occupancy of Balmoral by the military authorities during the Second World War, there were some compensations. Effective sewers were non-existent in 1930, but this was largely rectified when The King's Hall was built. During the military occupation, increased sewers became necessary and action was taken by the War Department, thus saving the Society a heavy outlay.

The Londonderry Hall, 600 feet long, was converted into an Aircraft Spar Boom shed; after the Society had pointed out to the Ministry of Supply that the wooden roof trusses were unsafe in the event of a snow storm, the entire tarred and felted wooden roof was replaced by corrugated asbestos and steel roof trusses. The roof was raised by about three feet and a level concrete floor was put in, as well as new electric lighting. The cost was over £10,000. The drainage of paddocks, and similar work, was carried out by the Society's workmen, both pre-war and post-war.

The Londonderry Hall was transformed into an Aircraft Spar Boom shed during the Second World War – vastly different from its normal usage as cattle stalling accommodation during the Annual Show.

The Harberton Hall, erected as a Components Production Store and Offices by the Air Ministry, was taken over by the Society as part compensation for the occupation and was converted to provide a Cattle Hall, a restaurant and a Poultry Hall. The Balmoral Restaurant, erected as a works canteen, was also taken over as part compensation. Various buildings erected during the occupation, including a suite of toilets and washing facilities on the Cattle Rings, emergency water tanks, and air raid shelters, were not of any use to the Society and were demolished. Overall, the Society's claim for compensation and damage as a result of the military occupation, amounted to more than £100,000.

The Victory lamp (a replica of Florence Nightingale's lamp), was presented to the Society in recognition of the sterling work undertaken during World War II in collecting Rural Pennies for the Red Cross Agricultural Fund.

The requisitioning of the Showgrounds during the War did not mean that the Society's staff were idle. Secretary Manager, Sam Clarke was recalled by the Linen Trade for flax growing propaganda for the war effort and the Linen Trade paid for the use of the Society's offices and the services of the staff to undertake this work. In 1943 Sam Clarke took over the organisation and running of the Rural Pennies section of the Red Cross. The work was done mainly at weekends and over a two year period until the end of the war. The magnificent sum of £41,280 was raised. A silver Florence Nightingale lamp was presented to the Society in recognition of this effort and this lamp can still be seen adorning a wall of one of the Society's offices.

By 1945 the Society and its Balmoral premises had survived two World Wars and a period of sustained economic depression. The Society, like Northern Ireland itself, was emerging from the shadows of conflict to more than two decades of comparative peace, and hope, in the stormy history of Northern Ireland.

NOTES

1 The Northern Ireland Economy by David S Johnson (An Economic History of Ulster 1820-1939, edited by Liam Kennedy and Philip Ollerenshaw and published by the Manchester University Press, p.191)

2 op.cit p.197

3 op.cit p.199

4 op.cit p.217

5 See Chapter Two

Digging for Victory

Leslie Martin, of the Countryside Management Division, Department of Agriculture, writes about agriculture during World War II.

"Food shortages: more production urgently needed from Northern Ireland's farmers." A misprint? No, a plea made during World War II. Agricultural production became crucially important as enemy action isolated the British Isles from food and feed imports. The story of the magnificent response of Northern Ireland's farmers in increasing production under difficult conditions was featured in the DANI exhibition at the 1995 Balmoral Show. This was a timely tribute to our agri-food industry, as the Show was being held in the same week as the VE Day celebrations.

War-time photographs (most of which had never been displayed before), posters and other articles – even the detested ration coupons! – recreated the atmosphere of the time, to enlighten the 'younger' generations and evoke memories for the older.

U-BOATS V THE FARMER

"Our ploughs are mightier than the German submarine" – so went one of the slogans of the time. Most of the United Kingdom's food was imported and thus vulnerable to enemy action, especially to U-boat attacks on merchant shipping. Shortages resulted, and food rationing had to be introduced.

It was quickly realised that more home food production was a top priority if victory was to be achieved. The public was urged to 'Dig for Victory' by growing some of their own vegetables. However, the main responsibility to feed the nation and its armies lay with the agricultural industry. Farmers, demoralised after the 'depression' years of the 1930s, were galvanised into action.

WINNING THE BATTLE

The loss of imported animal feed threatened home production of meat, milk and eggs. Farmers successfully met the challenge and by 1941 an additional quarter of a million acres of arable crops were being grown, mainly oats and potatoes. The oats were mostly used to replace the lost animal feed imports. The increased cropping reduced the amount of grassland available, but increased numbers of grazing livestock (measured in cow equivalents) were achieved. Stocking rates increased by more than 20%. It was thus possible to increase supplies of meat (even though sheep and pig numbers declined) and milk. Poultry numbers also increased significantly. The farmer had won his battle: the long hours, often spent under difficult conditions, had paid off.

Many factors contributed to increased production, not least the farmers' dedication and determination, assisted by guidance and advice from the Ministry of Agriculture. Crop production had the added 'persuasion' of The Compulsory Tillage Order, as well as Ploughing-Up Grants. However, the problem still remained of how to cope with the extra tillage work needed. As a result of the depression, most farms were poorly equipped and war-time availability of new farm machinery was limited. Fortunately, 'Lease-Lend' equipment from America became available in 1941.

Among the American imports – or at least those which evaded the enemy submarines and planes – was the Ford Ferguson tractor. This had Ulsterman Harry Ferguson's three point linkage and hydraulic lift, previously only available on the relatively rare Ferguson Brown tractor. The system was particularly suitable for ploughing and helped cope with the additional work needed. The rapid mechanisation of our agricultural industry had begun!

Parachutes and aeroplane fabric

The farmers' contribution to the war effort was not limited to food production. Locally produced flax was the main material in parachutes, aeroplane fabric, canvas and related products. Flax production and processing was concentrated in the North of Ireland: it was to Ulster's farmers that the Royal Air Force made a direct appeal for more flax for parachute webbing and harness early in the war. Acreage grown rose from 21,000 at the start of the war to a peak of 125,000 acres. More than 250 million square yards of linen products were supplied to the Services for a wide range of uses. Forestry also provided an important material for the war effort. Demand increased, but imported supplies declined. Heavy fellings were made in Northern Ireland's woodlands.

It was a time when everyone worked well together. Partnerships forged then are still helping the industry today. A strengthened Ministry of Agriculture was encouraging the adoption of new practices, teaching new skills and increasing efficiency. 'District Tillage Officers' were appointed at the outbreak of war, and were in close contact with farmers. Their responsibilities included advice and teaching in Winter Agricultural Classes. These were held in local centres and were well attended by farmers and members of their families. It was at this time that two of the most important developments in agriculture this century received a boost: silage and improved animal breeding.

Research was taking place in all aspects of production, especially at the Agricultural Research Institute, Hillsborough, while animal health was safeguarded.

The war introduced rapid change to agriculture, and farmers have continued to adapt quickly to new practices and marketing demands. A great deal was achieved under difficult circumstances, earning our farmers a well deserved place in history.

This fascinating map, which hangs in the Society's offices was dedicated to Sir Basil Brooke, the then Prime Minister of Northern Ireland, and depicts the agricultural scene in the Province during World War II.

PEACE AND PROGRESS

Chapter 4

THROUGHOUT THE PERIOD AFTER THE Second World War, agriculture remained the Province's largest industry. However the increased mechanisation on the farms led to job losses, and the Government was keen to attract inward investment not only to provide alternative employment for those coming off the land, but for others who had lost their jobs in the declining industries such as linen, at a time when the population of the region was increasing.

This fine example of a Beef Shorthorn Bull was exhibited at the 1947 Show by Capt. Alex Hill Dickson who, in addition to being a major cattle exhibitor, was also Chief Steward of the Ridden Hunters.

The Royal Ulster Agricultural Society itself made healthy progress after the Second World War. The 1947 Show, the first for several years, witnessed a marked renewal of interest. A total of 714 new members were added to the annual Membership Register, and 19 new Life Members were elected. The Annual Reports of these years reflect the growing momentum. The summary for 1948 noted that The King's Hall was back in use for Exhibitions, Boxing Championships and other activities, and a major highlight of the 1949 Show was a visit from the young Princess Elizabeth and the Duke of Edinburgh.

The Annual Report of 1950 recorded that the Society was well on its way to reaching its target of 5,000 members, though, sadly, the next year's Annual Report noted the death of Sir Milne

HRH Princess Elizabeth was a most popular Royal Visitor to the 1949 Annual Show. She was accompanied during her tour of the Showgrounds by the President Sir Milne Barbour.

Barbour who had been the Society's distinguished President for some 26 years.

The catalogues of the earlier Shows after the Second World War provide glimpses of a social world that has long gone. A '1st Class' meal in the Luncheon Room and New Canteen cost 6s 6d, but the Room upstairs was reserved for Judges, Stewards and Officials only (till 3.00 pm). Over in the Harberton Restaurant, opposite the Canteen, grooms and herdsmen made do with luncheons, suppers and breakfasts at 3s 6d. Meanwhile the work of the Show went on, and the 1948 Catalogue (price 2/6d) revealed on Page 34 that the Judge for the Kerry Classes 39-42 was none other than "Senator The McGillicuddy of the Reeks, The Reeks, Beaufort, Co Kerry".

Music has always been an attraction at the Show, and the 1951 Catalogue noted the presence of the Band of the Royal Marines, Plymouth under their Director of Music Captain RH Stoner. As well as the usual selection from Gilbert and Sullivan, and 'The Irish Washerwoman', the Band played a special item "When it's Apple Time in Armagh". The music of this was written by a Mr AE Logan, an Ulsterman living in Dublin, to mark "Festival of Britain Year". The sentiments were laudable, but "Apple Time in Armagh" as a musical item, seems to have sunk without trace!

The Annual Show during Coronation Year was held from 27-30 May 1953, with the music provided by the Band of the 1st Battalion the Royal Inniskilling Fusiliers who played appropriately the "Sprig of Shillelagh" and other regimental marches. The RUC Band played under its still-remembered District Inspector A Hollick, and featured its familiar and appropriate march past "The Young May Moon." The Catalogue advertisers, as ever, were abreast of events and "Cooper Products" of Herts noted that Coronation Year marked a new Chapter in British history. It also noted that new chapters were also beginning in the story of Cooper's research and achievements in the service of agriculture. "To Coopers Fly Dip, PTZ, Louse Powder, Pig Worm Powder, Aerosol Flyspray and the many other well-known and trusted Cooper defences for the farmer, are being added further products to promote the welfare of sheep, cattle, pigs and poultry." Even Debonair Cleaners of 173 Ravenhill Avenue, Belfast joined the band-wagon by announcing "The Coronation Festivities will demand that you appear at those functions you will attend looking smart and trim!" No doubt Her Majesty, on the eve of her Coronation, was suitably impressed by such advertising!

The Show itself continued to stage particular attractions for visitors. The now defunct *Northern Whig* reported on 23 May 1957 that hundreds of spectators watched an exhibition of sheep shearing by the World Champion, a Mr Godfrey Bowen of New Zealand. The *Farmers Weekly* reported that Mr Bowen had broken a 19-year world record by shearing 456 sheep in a nine-hour day. According to the paper the main purpose of his visit, which was arranged by the British and New Zealand Wool Marketing Boards, was to instruct local farmers and shearers on his methods.

Godfrey Bowen, the record-breaking New Zealand sheep shearer, demonstrating his skill at the 1960 Balmoral Show.

Bowen approached shearing as a science and developed a style and method now known throughout the world as "the Bowen Technique" which has shown the way to bigger tallies combined with quality shearing. He personally taught his methods to fellow shearers in all major sheep countries, and not only did his technique improve their productivity but with the reduction of second cuts to the fleece and skin cuts to the sheep, the Bowen Technique has saved the wool industry many millions of pounds. He died on 2 January 1994, aged 71.

During the same Show in 1957, the *Belfast Telegraph* reported that the traditional white-washed Ulster country cottage was still very popular with visitors. "Many people watched Mrs Gertrude Hall and her sister Mrs Ethel Picton baking oat cakes, soda farls and bannocks of wheaten bread. Many younger generations of farming families find the open turf fires and ovens . . . as strange as the city children."

Concern had been expressed in 1959 about the bad state of repair of the pig buildings and it was agreed that their replacement could no longer be deferred. Plans were made to erect a new building, of somewhat progressive design, which could house the greater part of the pigs and sheep entered for the Annual Show. When the Belfast Provender Millers became aware of the Society's intention they quickly undertook to make donations covenanted for seven years, which practically repaid the £20,000 capital sum required. The new building was named the Alexander Hall in memory of the late Major CAM Alexander MC DL of Pomeroy, a Vice President of the Society who had devoted much of his time and energies to the work of the Pig and Sheep Committees, until his death in 1958. The Alexander Hall was formally opened on 20 May 1960 by the then Prime Minister, Sir Basil Brooke.

The Prime Minister of Northern Ireland Viscount Brookeborough performed the opening ceremony of the Alexander Hall at the 1960 Annual Show. Also present were (from left) Alderman Robin Kinahan, Lord Mayor of Belfast, Mrs C A M Alexander (wife of Major Alexander, after whom the Hall was named) and the President of the Society, Col. Alex Gordon.

Balmoral continued to play a role in reflecting the complex political history of its times. In the autumn of 1962 some 100,000 people packed the Showgrounds for the 50th Anniversary of the 1912 signing of Ulster's League and Covenant by which many thousands of Unionists

The Rev Martin Smyth, left, leads the platform party along the avenue of standards and colours in the Arena at Balmoral which was thronged for the 50th Anniversary Rally of the signing of Ulster's Solemn League and Covenant. Also in the platform party were the Prime Minister, Lord Brookeborough, Sir George Clark, Sir Norman Stronge, the Bishop of Connor, the Moderator of the General Assembly and the President of the Methodist Church.

underlined their determination to remain citizens of the United Kingdom in the face of moves to impose Home Rule on Ireland. On Easter Tuesday 1912, around 100,000 people had also crowded in to the Balmoral Showgrounds to support a resolution against Home Rule. The 1962 Anniversary looked uncannily like history repeating itself, although in more relaxed circumstances, at a time when Ulster was comparatively peaceful, given the mayhem that was to follow from 1968. The *Belfast Newsletter* reported that "Fluttering above the Showgrounds was the largest Union Jack in the world, measuring 48 ft by 25 ft – the same one which flew at the 1912 Rally." The paper also reported that around 50,000 members of the Orange Order and similar institutions had paraded through Belfast from Carlisle Circus.

> As usual it was a great outing for the younger generation, their only trouble seemed to be seeing the parade over the heads of the taller adults. But one young man who solved the problem was 12-year-old Michael Joy of Holywood Road . . . not for Michael the exertion of climbing onto a wall or shinning up a lamp-post. He merely nipped on to his home-made stilts brought along by his father and enjoyed the view from a perch two feet higher than anyone else.

Her Majesty Queen Elizabeth II speaks to World War I veterans when she visited the Showgrounds in July 1966 on the occasion of the Golden Jubilee of the Battle of the Somme.

The theme of Balmoral as a reflection of history was clearly evident yet again in 1966 when the Queen, accompanied by Prince Philip, reviewed on 4 July a parade of veterans from the First World War, to mark the Golden Jubilee of the Battle of the Somme which took place in July 1916. It was a dignified and moving ceremony, and heavy with irony in that many of the young men who had marched and demonstrated at Balmoral at the height of the Home Rule crisis to show their loyalty to Britain were the same young men who died or were wounded at the Somme. Anyone who has visited the Battle site cannot fail to be touched by the sense of youthful bravery and idealism, and also the senseless and wholesale slaughter of that terrible Battle amid the long war of attrition. The visit of the Queen and Prince Philip to Balmoral was a fitting tribute to the sacrifice of a whole generation of young Ulstermen, and also a reminder that the bereaved had to live with a lifetime of sadness about what might have been.

Another 50th Anniversary was remembered at Balmoral on 20th August 1995 when HRH The Duke of York was present at a Drumhead Service to commemorate VJ Day, the ending of World War II.

Balmoral was also the venue for another Golden Jubilee event when on Sunday 20 August 1995, His Royal Highness The Duke of York attended an impressive Veterans Review and Drumhead Service to commemorate VJ Day and the 50th Anniversary of the end of the Second World War.

Meanwhile, one of the significant developments at Balmoral in the Sixties was the decision to build a new Members' Room, of which the central feature was its distinctive octagonal shape, which later gave it the affectionate nickname of "The three-penny bit". The "old" Members Rooms designed in 1927 by TW Henry had long since been inadequate to meet the increasing needs of Members, and news of the new building was first announced on 14 December 1962, though the proposal had been mooted in the Society much earlier. The project was to provide a new suite of buildings adjoining The King's Hall on the Lisburn Road site, at an estimated cost which began at £60,000 and later rose to £75,000. Frazer and Company of Hillfoot Street, Belfast were appointed as the main contractor and the design of Architects, Ferguson and McIlveen later won a Civic Trust Class I Award. The main feature was an assembly or concert hall of approximately 5,000 square feet, to seat more than 700 people, for concerts, conferences and other events. The Council stated in its Press Release: "With its rather unusual shape and progressive design, this fine hall should prove a great asset to the Society and to the whole community as well."

Other spacious dining rooms and lounges were planned for the first floor, which would be attached to The King's Hall at balcony level. In this way the two buildings could be used in conjunction, thus providing a high degree of flexibility. The statement continued: "The buildings are of such a nature that considerable use can be made of them throughout the year, for educational and cultural activities, as well as for exhibitions and social functions."

In a key passage the statement expressed thanks to the Ministry of Agriculture, which had agreed to make "a substantial Government Grant" to assist with the capital cost". The Council also expressed "its appreciation to the Minister of Finance and to the Minister of Agriculture for the great measure of confidence the Government had shown in the Society's affairs, and especially for the interest taken in the Society by the Ministry of Agriculture."

However this was coded language, for it masked over what had been a considerable row behind the scenes as to the exact funding, if any, the Society should receive from the Government.

From March 1962 the row dragged on and a perusal of the letters some 33 years later reveals great in-fighting in the elegant language beloved of civil servants and ministers who wage long wars with memoranda and paper-clips. The Society was asking for a £25,000 Government Grant, but at one stage it appeared as if nothing would be forthcoming. The row was complicated by a separate Government suggestion that the Society might help with the development of an international standard sports stadium to mark the 50th Anniversary of the signing of the Ulster Covenant. (The very idea of such a project reflects the different attitudes of the Stormont Government and Ministers of those days, compared to the vastly changed circumstances of today.)

On 31 May 1962 the row came to a head when a senior civil servant wrote to say that there was no reason why the Government should grant aid the project. In spirited language he stated:

> I do not wish in any way to decry the valuable work which the RUAS is doing in the agricultural world, but the facts as we see them do not justify our translating our admiration for the Society's work into a subvention from the Exchequer. The main purpose of the Society's new proposals is to provide an assembly hall for lectures and conferences, which will be used as a dining room for members during Show Week, and provide income for the Society by letting for other functions. I do not deny the need for these facilities but they are hardly such as to warrant Government assistance.
>
> Moreover, an examination of the Society's finances does not suggest that refusal of a grant would lead to the project failing. When The King's Hall was built in 1932-1935 the Society had an overdraft at the bank and no real assets. The building was financed by a £50,000 loan from the Government at the normal rate of interest plus an increase in the bank overdraft. By the end of 1935 the Society owed this Ministry nearly £48,000 and its overdraft was over £13,000: it had no liquid assets whatever. If the Society could face such expenditure 30 years ago I find it hard to think it can not find £100,000 today when its liquid assets are high and its Show profits comfortable.
>
> This feeling was strengthened when I discovered that the Society was prepared to contribute up to 25% of the cost of a projected sports stadium at Balmoral. It is surely a little illogical for the RUAS to ask for a grant of £25,000 from the Government and a month later promise £15,000 for a project which has no relation to its aims and objects. I think you must agree that the corollary is obvious: if there is £15,000 to spare then the Society should devote it to improving its own facilities.
>
> I have discussed this case with my Minister who agrees that there is no case for grant towards the cost of the hall.

Needless to say, the row rumbled on between Agriculture and Finance and went right to the top, with the Society caught in the middle. Indeed one hapless Society official expressed himself "shocked and hurt" by the turn of events. There were yet more meetings and more lobbying, but the story had a happy ending. According to Farmweek which reported the announcement of the new members rooms, the Ministry of Agriculture "had shown their faith in this venture by giving a grant of £25,000." The Society received its grant after all, but not without an immense amount of lobbying and hard work. The correspondence, which at this remove seems slightly comical, though with undertones of a fierce struggle beneath the surface, puts paid to any notion that the Stormont Government was "a soft touch" for the Society, even though they had many interests in common.

The Society had other benefactors, and in June 1964 Mr ET Green donated the considerable sum of £20,000 to the new project which was to be known as "The Members' Rooms with the central feature named the ET Green Hall".

Mr Green had been associated with the Royal Ulster Agricultural Society for over 30 years, and had been a Member of Council since 1941 and Chairman of the Finance Committee since 1955. He served on many other Committees and was appointed Vice President in 1958.

Mr Green had a long and distinguished association with the agricultural industry. He had been President of The Young Farmers' Clubs of Ulster and Chairman of the Herbage Seeds Committee of the Ministry of Agriculture, and also founder Chairman of the Ulster Folk Museum. He was also a Vice President of the Northern Ireland Ploughing Association, a member of the Royal Dublin Society, and a member of the Rural Industries Development Committee, of which he was first Chairman. He was President of the Hillsborough and District Horticultural Society and had been associated with many enterprises in and around Hillsborough.

His company had erected an educational and advisory exhibit at Balmoral Showgrounds, and on the stand of ET Green Limited, one of the largest in the Annual Show, space was provided each year for comprehensive displays of rural crafts and other attractions.

Every hen lays a golden egg – or is it a golden three-penny bit? *Farmweek's* imaginative cover marked the completion of the building of the "new" Members Rooms in 1965.

The splendid new premises were opened in May 1965 by the then Governor of Northern Ireland Lord Erskine. The total outlay on the new buildings up to 31 December, 1964 was almost £90,000, but the total cost, including all furnishings, was estimated at £150,000, according to a *Farmweek* report of 25 May 1965. This was twice the original estimate of £75,000 in March 1962.

The new premises were well received, but the Society was not allowed to rest on its laurels. A *Farmweek* editorial of 25 May, 1965, titled 'Success can be too easy' noted, somewhat testily:

> The ninety-eighth annual Spring Show at Balmoral has attracted bigger entries of livestock than ever before, the attendance is confidently expected to be a record, and the usual forecasts of the "most successful Show in the history of the Royal Ulster Agricultural Society" will, from these standpoints, undoubtedly be proved correct.
>
> Big changes have taken place since the first Show was held in 1855. Then, and in its early years, it was a "farmers' Show," organised primarily for the exhibition of livestock with the trophies gained highly-prized – as they still are today – by the agricultural community.
>
> Modern buildings have gone up – the most recent the new Members' Rooms officially opened yesterday by Lord Erskine, the Governor – and, gradually, as Ulster became one of the most highly-mechanised agricultural countries in the world, more and more of the Show space was devoted to exhibiting the latest and best in mechanical aids to profitable farming.
>
> Today's Balmoral Show is also an event which has much to interest the urban dweller and the annual attendance figures prove that it secures a big proportion of its support, apart from the exhibitors, from town and city dwellers . . .
>
> But – and here's the rub – continued success has brought with it the apathy that often goes hand-in-hand with the organisation of an event that from the word "go" is assured of turning out well, so that on the livestock side – and it was on this that the Show was founded – there has regrettably been little effort made at keeping up with the times.
>
> There is much that can be criticised at Balmoral and many recommendations from responsible quarters have been ignored – not the least the imperative need for a drastic overhaul of judging standards.
>
> More and more emphasis, for example, is being placed by commercial farmers on the marketing qualities of beef animals as distinct from their appearance as true representatives of the breed and there is agitation for judging standards to be altered to take account of both.
>
> There are so many defects in the judging system for livestock, especially beef animals, that to attempt to list even a section of them would be to compile a litany of grievances – but, briefly, it is urgently necessary that it should be brought into keeping with modern requirements – with the real needs of modern agriculture.

> In preparation for next year's Show a special committee of the most go-ahead members of the RUAS, with perhaps representatives of the Ministry and other interested bodies and organisations, should be set up now to draw up a modernisation programme for the Royal Ulster. This could help to ensure that its very success does not kill the Spring Show for the agriculturalist and gradually transform it into a day out for urban dwellers with a farmer or two there to have a look at how the city folk are getting on.

Prizewinners from the herds of Ian Duncan (Nos 146 and 162) and Noel Lusby (172) on parade during the judging of the Ayrshire Championship at the 1965 Annual Show.

This did not, and has not, happened, and the Show has continued to maintain high judging and other standards. The number of entries at the 1965 Show was 2,296, with prize money of £5,286.16.0 – a far cry from the original Show of 1855 when there were 506 entries, with prize money amounting to £216. Incidentally, the entries for 1965 would have been higher but the classes for poultry, pigeons and eggs were cancelled due to disease restrictions. The 1966 Show was hampered by a shipping strike. According to the *Belfast Telegraph* of 26 May, this caused serious problems for many industrial salesmen. "The strike had left some stands with a lean and hungry look, and many had to pad out their display by stripping dealers show rooms." Nevertheless the Show was deemed a success, but the weather was not!

The Report of Council for 1966 relays the following sad tale:

> The month of May, 1966 will be long remembered for the high winds and heavy rainfall. During the weekend prior to the Show, wind of gale force blew down many of our portable structures and marquees, including the Fashion Parade tent. With the untiring efforts of the Society's ground staff and other contractors, all was in readiness on the Tuesday evening for the opening the following day. Unfortunately , a cloud burst delivered one inch of rain early on the Wednesday morning and when the Show opened the Jumping Arena was under several inches of water. As a result, for the first time in the history of the Society, Horse and Pony Jumping was not possible on the opening day of the Show. By the invaluable assistance given by the Belfast Fire Brigade Pumping Teams and our own Arena staff, all the water was cleared away on the Wednesday and we were extremely fortunate to be able to carry out the normal Jumping Programme on the remaining three days and, indeed, to fit in all but one of the Wednesday Competitions. The Cattle and Horse Judging Rings were also in a dreadful condition on the Wednesday – the main Judging day,

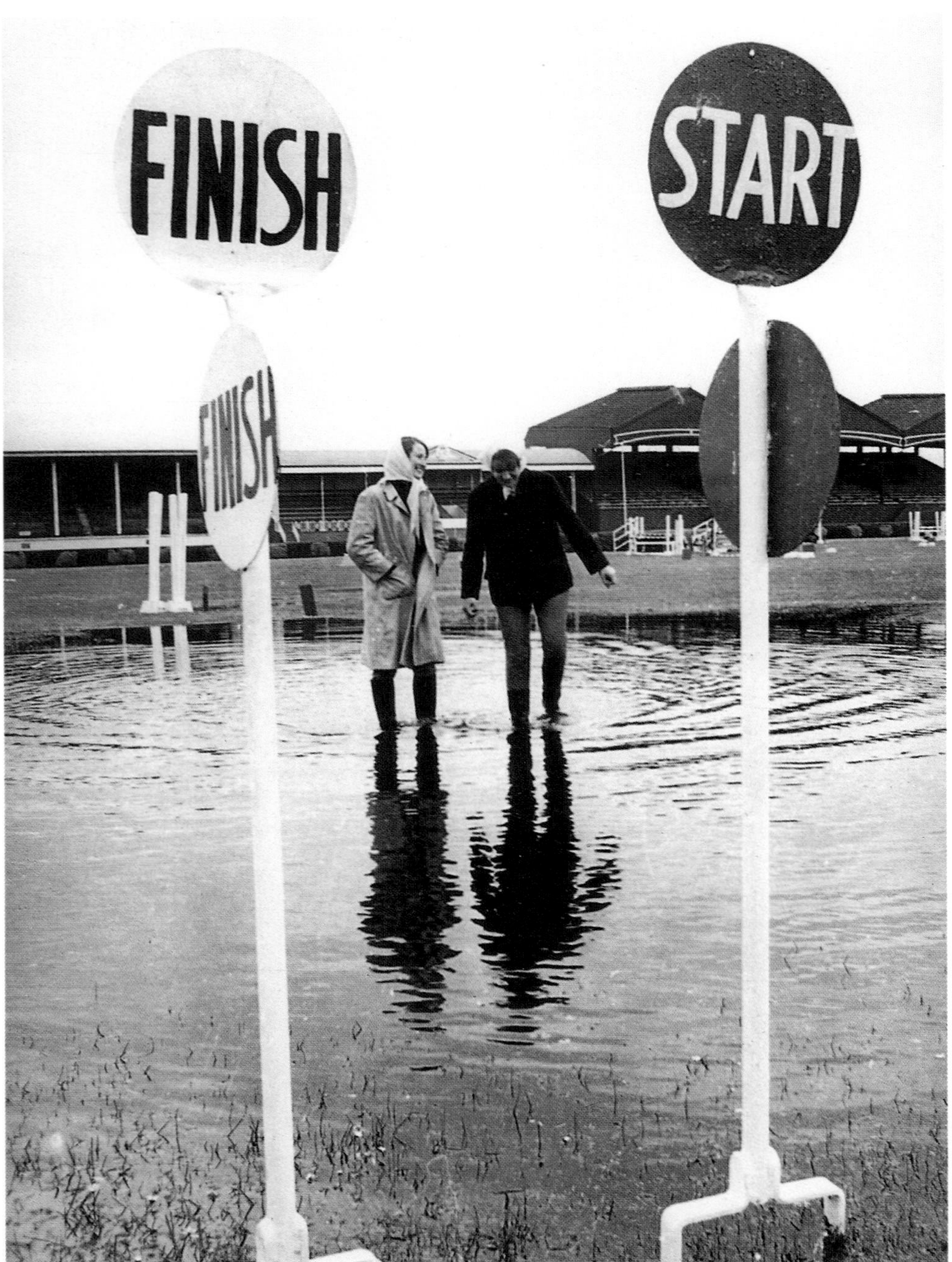

The weather always has a major influence on the success or otherwise of any Balmoral Show. This was certainly the case in 1966 when the Arena resembled a lake and the Fire Brigade had to be called in.

but, thanks to the work of the Society's Honorary Stewards and the co-operation of the exhibitors, the Judging programme was carried through as arranged. On the brighter side, Thursday, Friday and Saturday were favoured with good weather and, although our attendance was somewhat down on the Wednesday, the leeway was largely made up during the following three days.

The 1966 Show also had its element of surprise. *The Belfast Newsletter* of 27 May reported:

> A six man 'Red Devils' parachute team made a perfect four point landing in the main arena at Balmoral Showgrounds yesterday afternoon . . . but some spectators thought that a seventh had come a 'cropper'. It turned out however that it was only an unopened reserve parachute which had plummeted on to ground north of the enclosures. The parachute had been released by one of the sky divers as he made a free fall from 1,000 feet up.

The weather also played havoc with the spectacular Centenary Show of 1967. The Annual Report could not disguise the frustration of those whose high spirits had been dampened in this way.

> Unfortunately, the Show itself was seriously marred by exceptionally bad weather. From the beginning, May was one of the wettest months since records began and the continuous rain during the preceding weeks delayed preparations and placed a very great strain on the Society's staff prior to and during the Annual Show. Beginning with Sunday, on every day of Show Week and even during the nights there was very heavy rainfall. The first casualty was Show Jumping and it is with heavy regret that, for the first time in the history of the Society at Balmoral, it is recorded that there was no horse or pony jumping at the Annual Show. The horse, cattle, sheep and pig Judging Rings were also in very poor condition and well deserved tributes are due to the Stewards and Judges who managed somehow to carry through the judging programmes and keep them reasonably well up to time.
>
> Despite the weather, it was only just possible in the Jumping Arena to produce the Centenary Pageant under the direction of Brigadier Alasdair Maclean, CBE, from Edinburgh, along with Mr Kenneth Gilbert and Mr John Hall. With the assistance of massed military bands, contingents of military representing the Boer War, the Great War, and the Second World War, vintage and modern and agricultural and transport vehicles, period costumes, and by the spoken word, a presentation of the last 100 years was portrayed. Taking part in the Pageant were the Hunt Packs of the Newry Harriers with Master, Mrs MW Close, and the North Down Harriers, Master, Mr Granville C Nugent. These two Hunts lent considerable colour to the Pageant and the office bearers of the Hunts are greatly to be congratulated in carrying through their programmes under the most difficult circumstances. As a presentation, the Pageant was watched by large audiences who showed much appreciation, and as a spectacle some idea was given of the high standard of the production had the weather been more kind. It is ironical to place on record that the weather "took up" on the Saturday evening the Show closed and was followed by one of the best fortnights for many years.

The Centenary Show did have brighter moments as well, and the Annual Report concluded that "in many respects (it) was one of the most outstanding events ever held at Balmoral." On

Joseph M Thompson was proud to be President in 1967 when the Centenary Annual Show of the Society was held. He is photographed with his wife and son Courtenay. It is a neat coincidence that, twenty nine years later, Courtenay Thompson is President of the Society during the Centenary of the opening of Balmoral Showgrounds.

Friday, 26 May, Princess Margaret and Lord Snowdon paid an Official Visit – the day after the Standing Advisory Committee of the Royal Agricultural Society of the Commonwealth held its Annual Meeting at Balmoral under the Chairmanship of its President, Prince Philip. Clearly the RUAS took its "Royal" title seriously! The Centenary Show did create a sense of occasion with Royal visitors, special displays and widespread publicity, including voluminous newspaper Show Supplements which must have brought a flush of financial pleasure to their proprietors as well.

The success of the RUAS in these years reflected the atmosphere of relative peace and prosperity of Northern Ireland in the Fifties and Sixties, which were largely free of serious violence apart from a sporadic and ultimately abortive IRA border campaign. Few people at that time recognised the seeds of what was to become a quarter-century of the worst and most sustained violence in Western Europe since the Second World War. The Annual Report of 1968 took a backward glance at "the disastrous weather" during the Centenary Show, but concluded that "with fine weather, satisfactory entries and very large attendances each day, 1968 will go on record as one of the most successful Annual Shows held at Balmoral for many years."

There was similar sweetness and light in the Report for 1969, although the writer was still wary about the weather!

> The 102nd Annual Show was, in many respects, one of the most successful conducted by the Society. Apart from some light showers on Saturday forenoon the weather continued fine throughout the four days and the grounds and buildings presented a very pleasing appearance. The weather prior to the Show was very satisfactory and this enabled the Ground Staff to be well ahead with their preparatory work.

The 1969 Report, in retrospect, mirrors some of the enduring and re-assuring simplicity of much of life in the Province of those days, despite the deluge of violence that was to come. The Report noted that "entries in the livestock sections excluding horse jumping, at 2,653, were an increase of 271 over the previous year. The fine cattle entry of 410 was the highest at the Royal Ulster for many years, and the overall numbers in the horse, sheep and pig sections were at a very satisfactory level."

The Report noted that, for the first time, Horse Shoeing Competitions were held, and attracted an entry of fourteen blacksmiths, while "Classes for goats were re-introduced and attracted an entry of 24." The Report concluded:

> The fine weather, high level of livestock entries – some record numbers – and the very fine attendances each day, all combined to make the 1969 Annual Show an outstanding occasion, well up to and in some respects surpassing, the previous year's splendid Annual Show.

From the perspective of today, and knowing with hindsight the decades of terror and violence that were to disfigure and demean the Province later on, the cheery optimism of the 1969 Annual Report reads like a message from another world.

1

2

3

(1) Hugh C Kelly, who was Secretary of the Society from 1893-1897, and who masterminded the opening of Balmoral Showgrounds in 1896.

(2) Kenneth MacRae (Secretary 1897-1930) with his assistant John Nichol at the 1925 Cattle Show & Sale. (*Photograph: Irish Times*)

(3) Sam Clarke's era as Secretary of the Society stretched from March 1930 to his retirement in May 1958. He was dismayed on his arrival by the very basic office facilities, and wrote in his diary – "The offices were located in a wooden hut and were lacking in everything required for efficient working, there was not even a typewriter or filing cabinet. The telephone was the most antiquated I have ever seen. The name of the Royal Ulster did not appear anywhere along the valuable Lisburn Road frontage – not even on the letter box, because there wasn't one!" In the photograph he is seen with another long serving employee, Miss Tillie Montgomery at the RDS Spring Show in 1949.

4

(4) James T Kernohan, Secretary/Manager, May 1958 – August 1978.

FULL CIRCLE *Chapter 5*

THE OUTBREAK OF WHAT PEOPLE EUPHEMISTICALLY CALL "THE TROUBLES" at the end of the Sixties may have been detected earlier by those observers with very sensitive political antennae. With hindsight, there have been many who claimed to have been aware of what could happen. At the time, however, the vast majority of the people of Northern Ireland – on both sides – had little or no idea of the prolonged violence and suffering which was about to begin. In 1968 that most distinguished of *Belfast Telegraph* editors Dr John E Sayers asked this writer (then a young reporter) to write a series of articles on the Civil Rights demonstrations which had culminated violently in Londonderry on 5 October that year, and on their aftermath. The series was called "The Fifty Days Revolution". Even such a worldly-wise editor as Jack Sayers had completely underestimated the real bloody revolution that was to take place, with more than 3,000 people killed, many thousands more injured, and with terrorist damage running into millions of pounds. The abnormality of bombs and bullets, road-blocks and security searches, and the constant blood-drip of daily violence in the news bulletins were so commonplace that they became a kind of macabre normality.

It is only by looking back from the comparative peace since the paramilitary ceasefires towards the end of 1994, that the scale of the previous 25 years abnormality stands out. The experience is something similar to that of a man who has been banging his head for a long time, and begins to realise that there is a life beyond a constant feeling of pain, tension and distress.

Against this general background of difficulty and danger most Northern Ireland institutions, like the people themselves, tried to carry on with life as normally as possible. In doing so, they displayed much collective and individual courage and ingenuity, and Northern Ireland won a great deal of admiration for its spirit of long-suffering fortitude. Courage there was, but people put up the signs "Business as Usual" largely because, in many cases, they had no real alternative. Many left. Others were driven out but a large number stayed put, in a Province that more than once teetered perilously close to what could have become an all-out civil war.

The work of the RUAS, and the Balmoral Show, continued almost uninterrupted in this complex, difficult and often grave situation. Attendances were affected to a degree that it is difficult to estimate; it is only since the ceasefires of 1994 that a significant influx of visitors from across the border has been noticeable, with the 1995 Show demonstrating the welcome return of old friends, and the arrival of many new friends for the first time. Given lasting peace and an improving economy, the continued success of the Balmoral Show in this respect seems assured.

Colourful labels were widely used during the Sixties and early Seventies to promote Balmoral Show.

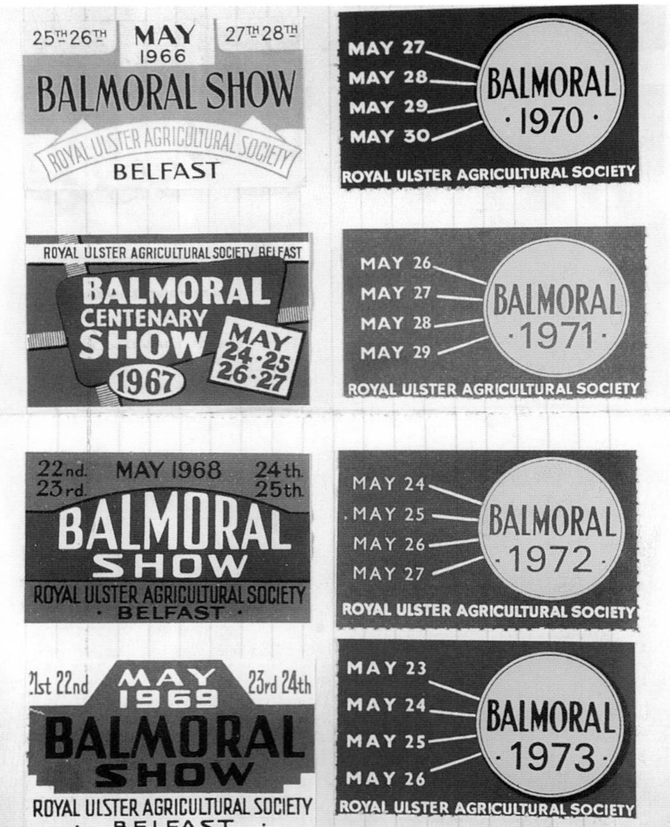

Away back in the early Seventies, however, the Annual Report recorded the normality of the Balmoral Show, and studiously ignored the mayhem that had the entire Province in its grip. Indeed the style of each Annual Report seemed to have been set in concrete, with each year's new statistics being slotted into a well-tried and somewhat tired formula. But the Troubles began to creep in. In 1972, one of the most violent periods of the entire period, with many deaths and injuries, the Annual Report noted that "The highlight of the year was again the 105th Annual Show. Despite unseasonably cold, wet weather and adverse effects from the troubled situation, a full programme of events was accomplished. The extremely cold weather and unsettled conditions at the time of the Show resulted in a drop in attendances. Nevertheless, Members of Council appreciated the wonderful support from so many organisations and considered that the Show was highly successful in the circumstances."

The Report also noted, in businesslike fashion, the start of the Balmoral Racing Pigeon Stakes, dog training displays on the Cattle Lawn, the "very popular sheep-dog demonstrations" . . . provided by Mr G Lionel Pennefather, and livestock entries of 2,537 compared to 2,104 the previous year.

The 1974 Report, however, recorded historic events, or to be more accurate, non-events. It stated:

> For the first time in the history of the Society owing to the strike conditions in the Province . . . the 107th Annual Show had to be postponed. This was a heavy far-reaching decision, and the bringing of our great organisation to a standstill and the reconvening the Show to the postponed dates represented a mammoth task to Members of Council and to all the staff.
>
> The President and Council would wish to place on record their deep sense of gratitude to all the livestock breeders and to the trade and industrial exhibitors who so willingly and effectively supported the Royal Ulster Show on the new dates. With this understanding and sympathetic attitude, the reconvened Show, whilst showing a fall in attendances, was regarded in the circumstances as a very successful event. Naturally, because of the change of dates, some exhibitors had to drop out, including the very attractive Fashion Shows by Robinson and Cleaver Ltd, and two of our main horticultural exhibitors who were unable to have materials available for the June dates.

The "Strike" referred to was the Ulster Workers' Council Strike which brought Northern Ireland to a standstill. It was organised and sustained by loyalist power-workers, shipyard workers and others who used the strike as a political weapon to bring down the Stormont Executive Government, which for the first-time in the history of Northern Ireland had a balanced representation from the Protestant and Roman Catholic communities. One of the particular targets of the strikers was the hated "Sunningdale Agreement" which under-pinned the work of the power-sharing Executive, and also proposed a Council of Ireland with representatives from Northern and Southern Ireland. This was seen by the Loyalists as unwarranted interference from Dublin, but again with hindsight it seems mild compared to the radical approach by the British and Irish Governments following the Anglo-Irish Agreement of 1985, and subsequent developments.

The Ulster Workers Council strike eventually brought down the Northern Ireland Executive largely through the massive intimidation of ordinary people who were prevented by force from going to their work. Electricity supplies were run down by the power-workers, and people had to cook with the use of solid fuel, and manage by candlelight. Buses were high-jacked, businesses closed and with the Government choosing not to break the strike by force, anarchy prevailed. By the end of May 1974, some two weeks after the strike had begun, the situation was so serious that the complete shut-down of electricity power to the Province looked inevitable, with catastrophic consequences. The situation, however, was not without its bucolic humour. Interviewed on radio, the President of the Ulster Farmers' Union was asked rhetorically if the agricultural industry was virtually on its knees due to the power strike? "On its knees?" replied the President incredulously "Sure its lying on the flat o its beck! . . ." Not surprisingly, the Balmoral Show, scheduled as usual for May, became a victim of the strike. Unfortunately, plans were so well advanced that the Show, in the face of threats and intimidation, had to be cancelled on the eve of the opening. Allen Anderson, then Chairman of Finance Committee and later President of the RUAS, recalls those difficult and dangerous moments.

"We were told by the Strikers that the Show should not take place. Even though all the animals were there, the very night before the opening, we were worried that if we carried on, the buildings would be machine-gunned.

I remember gathering together as many of the Show Committee as were available at such short notice. And we decided that the Show could not go on. Exhibitors and many other people were clamouring to know what was going to happen, and as Chairman I had to face the music. It was a straight choice between pressing on and calling the Strikers' bluff, or of defying them and putting lives at risk. So the decision was taken to postpone the Show. The immediate reaction was one of relief, particularly on the part of those exhibitors who were promised re-imbursement for their outlay. We postponed the Show until June that year, and thereby upset another Show up the country but there was little we could do about it."

The UWC Strikers, having brought down the Executive and helping to change the course of history, returned to the normality and abnormality of life in a Province in the middle of violent and political deadlock. The RUAS looked forward from the postponed Show of 1974 and reported in 1975 that "Our 108th Annual Show will take its place in history among the greatest Shows of the Society at Balmoral. The entries in the livestock sections were of record proportions, and splendid crowds attended on all four days. Along with the fine support from the livestock exhibitors and one of the best Trade and Industrial Displays ever seen at Balmoral, we were favoured with fine weather throughout. All these factors combined to make an outstanding Royal Ulster Show."

There was however a hint of special gratitude to those who rallied around in 1975, after the disappointment of 1974.

> The President and Members of Council again record deepest appreciation to all the livestock exhibitors, jumping competitors, trade stand exhibitors, and other organisations and companies whose combined efforts made the 108th Show an outstanding success. In addition, thanks are due to the general public for their continued support and the interest taken in the Society's affairs.

The success of a number of established King's Hall exhibitions and their need to expand led to the building in 1975 of a new 12,000 sq ft hall on the site of the machinery sheds at the rear of The King's Hall. Linked to that building by two corridors, the new facility was named the Nugent Hall in recognition of the sterling contribution to the work of the Royal Ulster by Granville C Nugent who in 1976 became President of the Society. The Nugent Hall was built so that it could readily be doubled in size, and in 1986 this happened with the enlarged Hall completed in time for the first Royal Ulster Winter Fair.

In 1977, the need to increase space for exhibition use switched to the need to decrease the size of the Arena which had become too large for modern show jumping. It was taking up valuable space which could be better utilised in providing trade stands. After lengthy consultation, the Horse Committee agreed to the re-design of the Arena providing a much more compact area and the smaller Grand Ring was first used at the 1978 Annual Show.

The 1978 Show, again a success, heralded an end of a long era of RUAS history with the departure of James Kernohan, who had been Secretary Manager since 1958. The Society has been more than fortunate in having Secretary Managers who have devoted a considerable portion of their working lives to Balmoral. Having seen the then North East Agricultural Association successfully through its first Balmoral Show in 1896, Hugh C Kelly passed over the reins the following year to Kenneth MacRae who remained in office for almost 33 years until his retirement in 1930. His successor, Sam Clarke, steered the Society through The King's Hall creation, the difficult times during the Second World War and well into the Fifties, retiring after 28 years service to allow James Kernohan to take over.

"James T" Kernohan, by all accounts was his own man and within his own territory, his word was law. He had his supporters and his critics, like any professional, but he was given a handsome tribute in the 1978 Annual Report:

> He came to Balmoral with a distinguished background in agriculture and he applied this knowledge to great effect in the affairs of the Society. He is a man of considerable patience, courage, comprehension and diplomacy and he applied these attributes to the benefit of the Society. During his term of office he pioneered a number of significant building developments including the Alexander Hall, the new Members Rooms, the Granville Nugent Hall and the Arena modifications. The dramatic increase in the use and in the recognition of The King's Hall as the major Exhibition Centre in the Province is in no small way due to his efforts. The present healthy position of the Society's finances are a fitting tribute to his hard work over the years.

As a token of their appreciation, the Society presented James Kernohan with a salver and a cheque at a function in the Members' Room in December 1978, and Council wished him a long and happy retirement. Sadly, however, his retirement was prematurely cut short by his death on 13 September 1980.

William H Yarr, known to his friends as Billy but rechristened on his arrival at Balmoral by the media to the more business-like name of "Bill", brought a very different style to the newly-created post of Chief Executive. An Honours Chemistry graduate of the Queen's University of Belfast, he had spent 18 years in the textile business where he rose to Director in charge of Marketing, Sales and Product Development of the Doagh Spinning Company. His commercial and business experience was further strengthened by a three year term with LEDU, the Local Enterprise Development Unit where he was Development Manager and Deputy Chief Executive.

The present Chief Executive seen with James Pollock (President), at the 1992 Annual Show celebrating the Award of the Belfast Telegraph Cup to Bill Yarr for his contribution to Northern Ireland Agriculture. (Photograph: Wilfred Green)

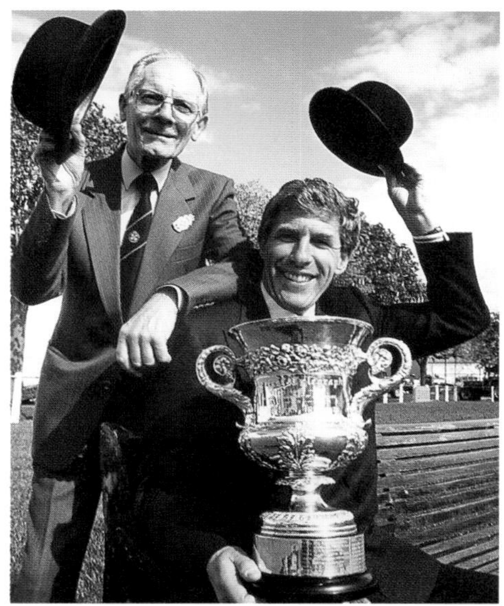

Bill Yarr, who was born and brought up in Belfast, had travelled widely in Europe in the textile business but he had no direct experience of agriculture. One of the first tasks at the RUAS was to listen and to learn, and to make himself known to as many members as possible. This he did with typical thoroughness and precision, and he steadily built a reputation as one of the most popular and effective Secretary Managers and Chief Executives in the history of the Society. He quickly became aware of the need to maintain a working balance between the various interests in the Society and the system dating from 1980 of co-opting new members to Council was a significant reform. It helped to maintain the necessary balance and to introduce new blood into the governing body. His tenure of office from 1978 to this time of writing has brought a significant expansion in the income of the Society, a comprehensive upgrading of facilities, a considerable increase in the commercial activities, and a consolidation in the already high reputation of the Society. All of this progress has been achieved during a period characterised by sweeping changes in the fortunes of the agricultural industry, a prolonged industrial recession and the constant violence and disruption of the Troubles.

One of Yarr's first priorities was to establish a firm financial base. The Society's nett current assets excluding buildings and land in 1978, when he took over, were £61,000 – not a bad figure by the standards of the time. By 1994, the nett assets had risen to £1.3m, and this significant increase has to be seen against an expenditure of some £4.5m from 1978-1994 in upgrading facilities throughout the Balmoral complex.

The buildings were classed technically as "assets" but by the late Seventies many were in various stages of disrepair and were virtually "liabilities". Urgent work was needed to repair the roof of The King's Hall, and this began in the summer of 1981. The main contractors for the work were H and J Martin Ltd and the job which was undertaken in 2 phases (June to September 1981 and June to September 1982) involved the removal of the existing reinforced concrete roof and its replacement with a blue and grey profiled steel covering. It is of interest to note that whilst the total cost of building The King's Hall in 1935 was £61,000, the cost of replacing the roof 46 years later was £750,000.

The 1980 Annual Report underlined the huge financial challenge to the Society. It stated: "There is little doubt that the project will impose a severe strain on the Society's finances, and will require considerable outside assistance. To this end a special "President's Appeal" is being launched, and the support of Members and friends of the Society will be much appreciated." A £600,000 "Development Appeal" was duly launched in the Spring of 1982, based on anticipated expenditure included in a five-year development plan. The Appeal raised some £350,000 and together with a grant-aid of £400,000 from the Department of Agriculture, the Society was able to undertake a comprehensive refurbishment of many of the Balmoral facilities. Together with income from commercial activities, the Society had sufficient funds not only to repair The King's Hall roof but also to re-roof the Alexander Hall, to build additional livestock accommodation, to upgrade judging facilities, to replace perimeter fencing and to improve many of the roads within the Showground complex. The installation of new boilers and a much-improved heating system in The Kings Hall was also undertaken, as was a start to the much-needed refurbishment of furnishings in the Members' Room.

Before and After!
These two photographs clearly show the dramatic change in the profile of the roof of The King's Hall following the major repair work undertaken in 1981 and 1982.

Having completed the "five year plan" in 1986 a follow-on five year development phase was initiated, and with financial assistance from the EEC Regional Development Fund (linked of course to income from commercial activities), a new Foyer and outer canopy was provided at the front of The King's Hall, as well as the widening of The King's Hall balcony, the installation of tiered seating units for use at concerts, the upgrading of the four stairwells, and the doubling in size of the Nugent Hall.

The Annual Report of 1990, outlined firmly the importance of the Society's commercial activities in generating funds to maintain the suite of Balmoral buildings and facilities in good condition. It noted:

> The importance of income generated from exhibitions, concerts and boxing is significant for it allows the Society to fund the upkeep, maintenance and development of the Showgrounds. Over the past ten years, more than £3 million has been spent in refurbishment and modernisation of buildings and facilities and whilst it is not denied that substantial expenditure has been directed towards The King's Hall Complex, it must be understood that projects like the building of the Alexander Hall extension for pig accommodation, the erection of the Sheep Fold, the maintenance and restalling of the Londonderry Hall and the redrainage of the Cattle Lawn and the Arena just would not have been possible without the Motor Shows, the Fun Fairs, the Dave Boy McAuleys and the Cliff Richards.

The need for maintenance and refurbishment is ever present, and work completed during 1995 included the refurbishment of the hospitality suite at the Royal Grand Stand, the installation of air conditioning in the Balmoral Conference Centre, the provision of a passenger lift to serve the balcony of The King's Hall, the modernisation of toilet facilities on that level and the replacement of a portion of bench type seating with moulded seats – at a total cost of more than £250,000. As the Chief Executive notes: "The main objective of the Society is the promotion of agriculture, and without the Balmoral Show there would be no Society. However, without the commercial activity, there would be insufficient funds to sustain the work of the Society. The upgrading of our facilities in the past 16 years has been very costly, but the improvements have enabled us to become much more professional in the range of services we can offer. This, in turn, has helped to generate much-needed new income."[1]

Undoubtedly the need for continuing refurbishment will continue, and one such project is the consideration of an extension to the first floor bar lounge area in the Conference Centre to provide more space for members of the Society during Balmoral Show.

The Troubles continued to cast their shadow over Northern Ireland throughout the late Seventies, the Eighties and the early Nineties. The RUAS suffered directly with the cancellation of the Ideal Home Exhibition in 1972 and the postponement of the Show itself in 1974 due to the Ulster Workers' Council Strike. However one of the worst outrages occurred in 1988 when the Provisional IRA planted and exploded a bomb at the RUC Stand during the

Children among the casualties

BOMB BLAST AT THE ROYAL SHOW

This banner headline brings back horrendous memories of those who were caught up in the outrageous no-warning terrorist bomb which exploded on the Thursday evening of the 1988 Show.

Balmoral Show. The *Daily Mail* ran a page one story the next day with the headline "Bomb Blast at the Royal Show" and reported that "at least a dozen people were hurt, including two brothers aged 9 and 13. Three policemen were among the casualties." The *Belfast Telegraph's* lead story featured the IRA's claim that it had been responsible, and the incident was widely condemned. The Chief Executive resolutely refused to be drawn by reporters on questions of security, and noted phlegmatically to the *Irish News* "This is the 121st Show, and I am sure there will be a 122nd!" Despite the worrying headlines, Michael Drake, the agricultural correspondent of the *Belfast Telegraph* stated: "Notwithstanding what happened on the night before the Show ended, all who attended must agree it was a bumper, bumper event. That was Balmoral, a Show with everything for anyone and anything for everyone. It was one of the best I remember in over a decade of walking the Showgrounds."

The Annual Report of 1988 put the whole matter in perspective.

> No-one who was in the Showgrounds at 8.00 pm on the Thursday of the Show will readily forget the terrorist attack on the Royal Ulster Constabulary stand situated in the heart of the Showgrounds. Hundreds of people were in the immediate vicinity of the no-warning bomb and it was a miracle that the casualty list was not much higher than the twelve people who were admitted to hospital.
>
> The Council expresses its regret that the Balmoral Show was attacked in such a callous way and with a complete disregard for the safety of those attending and sympathy is expressed to all who were injured or inconvenienced by the explosion.
>
> After a hard night's work and with the support and co-operation of many, the Show re-opened the following morning as scheduled for "business as usual" with minimal evidence of the mayhem of the previous evening. Undoubtedly, the bomb had an adverse effect on the attendance of the last day but overall the total attendance, published as 80,000, was increased over last year and this was a most gratifying reward for all the endeavours put into the arrangements for the event.

Incidentally, the 1988 Show also made good headlines by re-introducing International Show Jumping to Balmoral for the first time in 15 years. This was a huge success, with nine top class riders from Great Britain (including Harvey Smith) competing with the best riders and horses from Ireland for a then record £17,000 prize fund.

The unrest, and the recession, took a toll in other ways. As the Troubles deepened, many people felt less inclined to travel to Belfast with the risk of violence and the near-certainty of road-blocks. A number of livestock marts were established in rural areas, and the cattle sales at Balmoral suffered accordingly. In 1978 some 223 cattle and 154 pigs had been purchased at the Spring Sales, but by the mid-Eighties the numbers of cattle had decreased dramatically, and by 1989 the cattle sales had petered out. This was offset, however, by the continued strength of pig sales at Balmoral, which was able to provide a disease free environment, and by 1989 Pig Shows and Sales had increased from two to three a year. The 1989 Annual Report noted that at the Autumn Sale "the staggering sum of £13,500 guineas was paid for the Landrace Boar exhibited by Cyril Millar of Coleraine – this figure is a record for Balmoral and may well be the highest price ever paid for a pig in the British Isles or further afield."

There were other notable success stories including the establishment of the highly successful Winter Fair, which began in 1986. This arose out of an acclaimed indoor Show in December 1984 as part of the 75th Anniversary Celebrations of the Northern Ireland British Friesian Breeders' Club. The 1986 Winter Fair was primarily dairy orientated, with showing classes included for Dairy Shorthorns, Holstein Friesians, British Friesians, Ayrshires and Jerseys, and the Fair, sponsored by the Northern Bank, is still going strong. The 1993 Winter Fair, for example, attracted 4,000 visitors, and in the words of the 1994 Annual Report "In the run-up to Christmas, the atmosphere of the Winter Fair must be experienced to be believed." As well, the Society stages a Pig and Poultry Fair every two years, which is also very successful.

Many events have been held in The King's Hall over the years, but few equal the atmosphere created at the dairy-orientated Royal Ulster Winter Fair which has been a regular feature in December since 1986 – even the sawdust in the judging ring is dyed green to provide the grass effect! (Photograph: John Harrison)

On the wider front the Society remains aware of the need to promote the agricultural aims of the Show, not only locally but further afield. In the mid-Eighties, three of the national Royal Agricultural Societies – the Royal Highland, the Royal Welsh and the Royal Ulster and later joined by the Royal Agricultural Society of England – combined to form "CARAS", the Council for Awards of Royal Agricultural Societies. The object was to provide distinctive Awards of Merit (Associateships and Fellowships), to encourage young people to develop their full potential and to recognise achievement in Agriculture in the widest sense. From a standing start of zero in 1985, within ten years, 29 Fellows and 41 Associates from Northern Ireland have achieved the required standard and have been recognised accordingly. The RUAS, ever-conscious of the need to encourage co-operation between related organisations, has given its full backing to the development of the Northern Ireland Shows' Association which provides an important forum for all Agricultural Shows and their Officials and Committee Members from Northern Ireland. The RUAS also continues to recognise the work of Queen's University in training agriculturalists of the future – it sponsors the Agrarian Society of Northern Ireland in bringing top-class speakers to the Province to take part in their Annual Lecture programme, while it provides an annual Medal and cash award for the top General Agriculture student who graduates each year. The RUAS is also an active member of the Royal Agricultural Society of the Commonwealth and regularly sends delegates to its biennial conferences in many parts of the world.

Prince Philip who has been President of the RASC since its inception in 1957, takes a keen interest in its activities and invariably attends the biennial conferences. In 1967 he chaired a meeting of the Advisory Committee which was specially arranged as part of the celebrations for the 100th Show organised by the RUAS. It is therefore appropriate that following the 1996 Conference in Chester, the post-conference tour of delegates and their partners will spend 5 days in Northern Ireland on dates which exactly coincide with the first Show held at Balmoral in 1896.

The RUAS is also affiliated to the Association of Shows and Agricultural Organisations which encompasses all agricultural Shows in the British Isles. Bill Yarr, who was Chairman in 1989 and 1990, organised the Annual Conference in Belfast, when some 100 delegates representing more than 50 Shows experienced the expertise and hospitality of their agricultural colleagues in Northern Ireland. Still on the wider promotional front, the RUAS played an integral role in the British Food and Farming Year 1989 with special initiatives in Northern Ireland.

The year 1989 was designated as British Food and Farming Year. The Royal Ulster co-ordinated the Celebrations in Northern Ireland, and the main attraction at the Balmoral Show was a stunning exhibition housed in a massive geodetic marquee at the south end of the Arena. It was titled "5000 Years of British Farm Animals".

A significant development in recent years has been the relationship between the Duke of Edinburgh Award Scheme and the Society. Not only are Silver Award Presentation ceremonies staged at Balmoral but assistance has been provided to the Young Farmers Clubs of Ulster to encourage their members to participate in the Award Scheme. There is no doubt that achievement of Gold or Silver awards by young farmers will be to the future benefit of the Northern Ireland agri-food industry as a whole.

Whilst the relationship with the Duke of Edinburgh Award Scheme may be relatively new, the same cannot be said of the relationship between the Royal Ulster and the Royal Dublin Society. This has existed for very many years and is as strong now as it ever has been with regular contact made at both Officer and Executive level on matters of mutual interest.

In essence the RUAS has covered an extremely wide spectrum in its activities, ranging from commercial projects to promotional activities for agriculture in general, but its flagship activity still remains the Balmoral Show which through the Eighties and Nineties has remained a vibrant centrepiece of its year.

The Annual Reports bear faithful witness to all the major developments, and these publications themselves have improved with the march of time and new technology. The first photographs were introduced in 1983, a new cover with a black and white photograph was featured in 1986, and two years later the first colour covers were produced, with an attractive design throughout the magazine.

The strong relationship between the Royal Ulster and the Royal Dublin Society is cemented annually by visits of Senior Office Bearers and staff to major events at both venues. During a visit of the Committee Chairmen to Ballsbridge in 1992, Professor Dervilla Donnelly, then RDS President, handed over this Crystal Plate to James Pollock to symbolise the relationship between the two Societies.

Over the years it is not just the major developments, but also the little snippets which catch the eye. The Show has constantly produced a wide range of "entertainers", including Red Rum, the famous Grand National winner, who died in October 1995, aged 30, the Cossacks, the Musical Ride of the Household Cavalry, the Meadow Stud of Working Donkeys, and the JCB "Dancing Diggers", as well as the exotically named winners such as Twilight Lin Anita, a Champion British Friesian Cow, Kilcurry Clara 38th, a Senior Landrace Sow, and a Chinese Goose!

Over the years, the style and content of the Society's Annual Reports have changed to make the publication more attractive, informative and readable.

Apart from producing such "entertainers" and "exotica", the Show itself underwent fundamental changes in recent years. In 1981 the 114th Annual Show marked a significant departure from tradition by commencing on a Tuesday and ending on Friday. This was due to falling attendances on the Saturday at previous Shows, due to the minimal level of trade carried out on that day. The 1981 Show organisers had other concerns on their minds:

The change in the days of the Show was, however, only one of the problems which those involved in the Show had to face. Whether organising, exhibiting or just spectating no-one could have failed to be affected by some of the most adverse conditions to hit the Show for years. The month of May had the highest rainfall recorded for over 60 years and torrential rain before, and during, the Show quickly turned the Trade Stands, Judging Rings and Arena into a sea of mud. This weather, together, with the Local Government Election voting taking place on the second day, in the main accounted for a decrease in attendance of approximately 20% over the Annual Show in 1980. The other main factor, of course, was the continuing (and worsening) economic depression. Although the Machinery Section had been hit very hard by this depression all Trade space was, nevertheless, taken up although very few exhibitors, at the end of the day, reported a record-breaking Show.

During the previous year the Show had been moved to a week earlier, at the request of the silage-makers, and the organisers were rewarded accordingly. The Annual Report for 1980 noted, unusually, that the weather had been so dry since Easter that "serious consideration" was being given to watering the judging rings and arena. It added: ". . . however, our prayers were answered with some heavy showers two days before the Show opened, to put the Grounds in perfect condition, and for the rest of the week we were blessed with beautiful sunny weather."

The other major change in the Show was a reduction to three days instead of four, which took place from 1991. The Annual Report stated: ". . . Accounting for the changing scenario and conditions in the agricultural industry, the decision was taken to reduce the duration by dropping the Tuesday opening . . . After the event, when all the dust had settled, the overwhelming opinion was that the change ... had been timely and well received. From an attendance point of view, we achieved the same numbers over three days as we did over four in 1990, and whilst the deepening of the countrywide recession was felt by many exhibitors, it was accepted that the new format provided them with the best opportunity to market their products and services."

RUAS announces sweeping changes in show format

THREE-DAY BALMORAL!

by FarmWeek Staff Reporter

MAJOR changes to the format of Balmoral Show were announced this week.

In 1991 for the first time the show will switch to three days, dropping the traditional Tuesday opening day.

At a press reception in Belfast, Mr. James Pollock, Royal Ulster Agricultural Society president, and Mr. Bill Yarr, RUAS chief executive, outlined the sweeping changes to the show.

In an effort to strengthen the event the show will run from Wednesday, May 22 to Friday, May 24 next year and will be open late every evening.

Mr. Yarr explained: "For some time we have been looking at the four-day format. In the early 80s we initiated a change from Wednesday-Saturday to Tuesday-Friday, when it was obvious that Saturday was not a day the public wanted to come to an agricultural show in Belfast.

"But we have never quite satisfied ourselves on the first day of the show. We thought it could have attained a much better attendance - but this never came about.

TIME

"In recent years," he said, "pedigree livestock farmers, whose animals contribute so significantly to the show, have found the time demands of a four-day event an increasing strain.

"Most beef breeders removed their animals from the showgrounds at the end of the third day, Thursday, leaving many of Friday's visitors understandably disappointed by the lack of stock on display.

"The result has been a reduction in visitor attendances on Fridays, something which greatly affected the general show atmosphere. As the show closed at 6p.m. on the last day, afternoon visitors were even less likely to make the effort to come."

Matters came to a head after this year's May show when dairy cattle breeders also made a strong case to the society to be excused attendance on the last day.

"If this were to happen, Balmoral would cease to be an 'agricultural' show in the full sense - an untenable position for the society," Mr. Yarr said.

It was disclosed, too, that exhibitors had expressed some dissatisfaction about low last-day attendances and consequential poor levels of interest in exhibits.

After many meetings within the society and with other interested parties, Mr. Yarr said the three day show format has been accepted as a step forward.

STATUS

He added that Balmoral had grown in status year by year and that the society, in making the changes, believed it was anticipating something which would have happened in five years time.

"On balance the Wednesay-to-Friday format is the best opportunity for the widest range of the Northern Ireland public to come to the show and enhance the status of the event", he said.

(Cont on 3)

Farmweek **announces a major development.**

It should be noted, however, that the change in format created considerable challenges for the organisers who had to cram a four day extravaganza into three, but the problems were overcome with style. Incidentally, the year 1991 was noteworthy also because of a visit by Prince Philip to the Showgrounds, the first such visit since 1967. Although his visit was not

Agricultural education plays an important part in the Royal Ulster's main objective of promoting agriculture and this extends to all ages. Specially produced booklets are issued to school children visiting Balmoral Show to help them understand the various exhibits on display. This young girl, Laura Carswell from Banbridge, is intrigued with a Longhorn cow on the Rare Breeds stand at the 1995 Balmoral Show. *(Photograph: Belfast Telegraph)*

to a Royal Ulster event, he did take time to have coffee with senior Society officers and staff and showed a considerable interest in the progress of the RUAS since his last visit.

The Show has encompassed many changes since it was first established as a two-day event in 1855, and the Centenary of the opening of Balmoral Showgrounds, provides not only a milestone but also an oppportunity for the Society to plan ahead. The approach of the Millennium and the possible availability of substantial sums of money, through the Millennium Commission [from the proceeds of the National Lottery], encouraged Council to commission the drawing up of a Masterplan for the future development of Balmoral.

The long-term strategy of this project was to create a facility, using the brand "Balmoral Event Park" as the working title and featuring:

> An agricultural Showground with the highest standard of facilities to demonstrate the pre-eminence of Balmoral Show and its role in promoting the Agri-food industry.
>
> A covered complex featuring the existing King's, Nugent and Balmoral Halls and introducing a new 10,000 seat indoor Arena with the capability of

providing an exciting venue for international sports events, concerts, family entertainment and exhibitions.

An outdoor stadium on the site of the existing Show Jumping Arena to be used not only during Balmoral Show but also for high profile sporting events throughout the year.

The existing Balmoral Conference Centre ideally integrated with a hotel development.

Related visitor services, car parking and transport arrangement.

A high-calibre parkland setting that conveys the international status of the "Balmoral Event Park" site.

Bill Yarr noted "Only time will determine how much of this strategy is achieved. What is clear, however, is that the legacy passed on by the forefathers of the Society has to be maintained, developed and passed on to its successors, and the present Council, are determined to ensure that no stone is left unturned in achieving this objective".

A typical scene during Balmoral Show with visitors thronging the Showgrounds as they walk, in warm sunshine, around the various farm machinery stands. The Showgrounds may be small in relation to other major national Royal Shows, but there is no doubt that the special atmosphere created is not repeated elsewhere!

As planning progresses for the Centenary Celebrations in 1996, the Chief Executive is clear that the Show itself must and will remain the flagship for the Society. "We need to keep it wide-ranging and attractive to the public, but the educational aspect is the primary objective of the Show. Farmers are given the opportunity to see the latest and the very best trends in livestock and machinery, and the research and development in the industry is well represented by the various Exhibitions that take place. We are underlining the statement that agriculture is the most important industry in Northern Ireland, we are saying to the public that they should be buying locally produced high quality food, that they should encourage people to enjoy and not to destroy the wonderful environment of our countryside, and we are encouraging those who do not know agriculture at first hand, and especially the young people to come and see the work of the industry and the significant contribution that it makes to the economy and well being of the Province. We have a good story to tell, and the Balmoral Show is one of the best ways of telling it."

NOTES

1 The Commercial activities of the Society are discussed in detail in the next two Chapters.

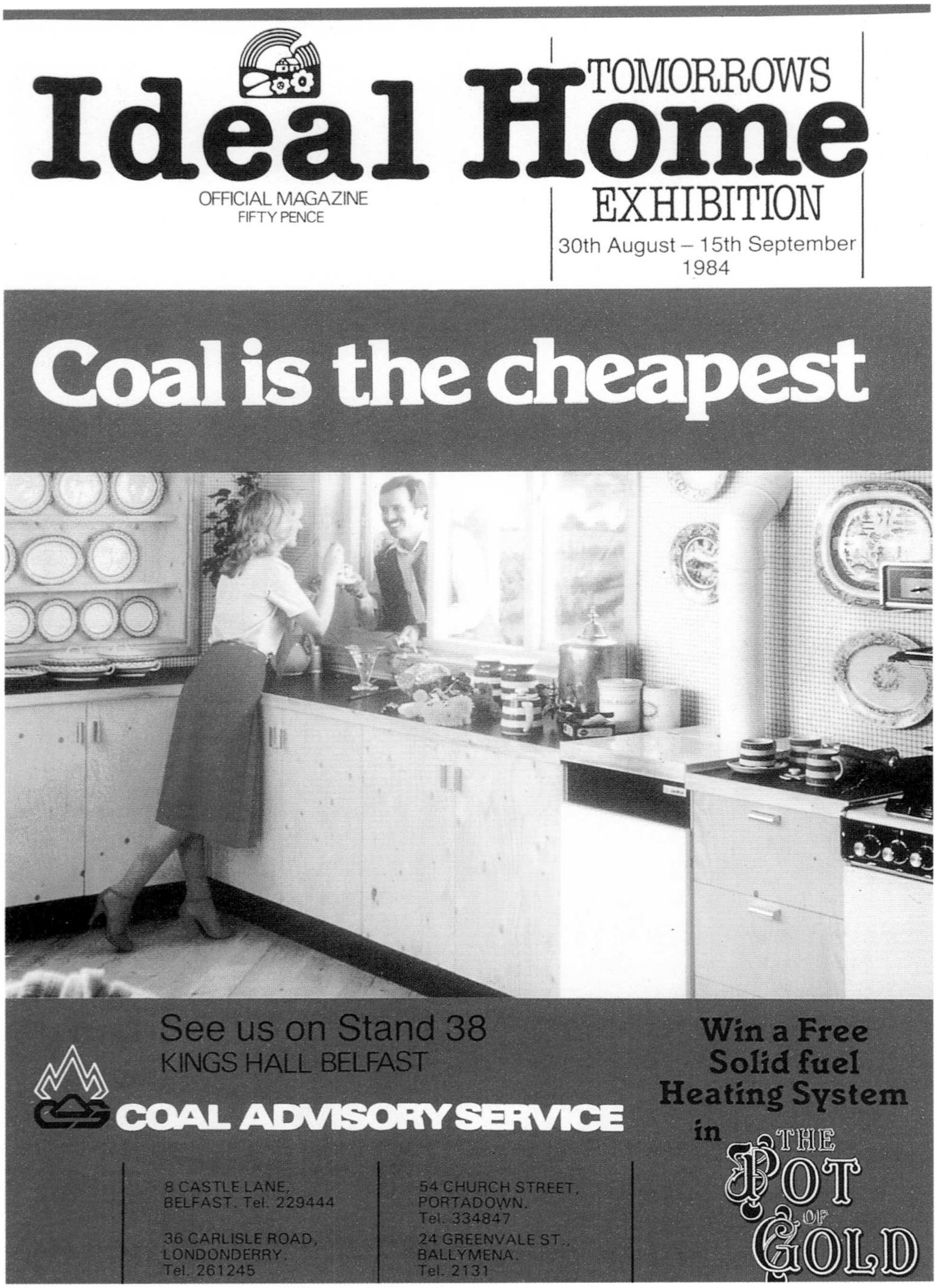

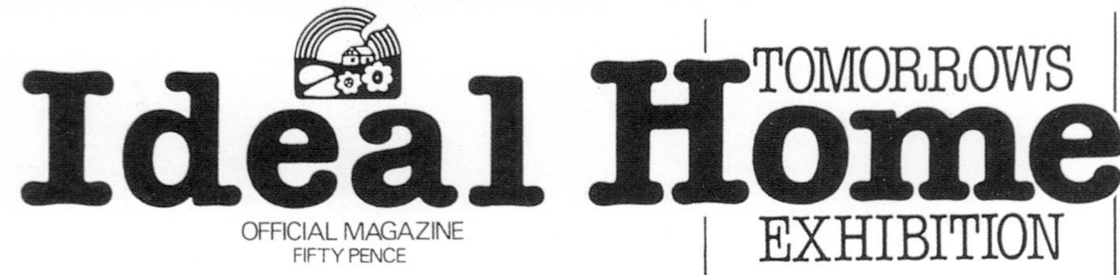

Ideal Home
TOMORROWS
EXHIBITION
OFFICIAL MAGAZINE
FIFTY PENCE
30th August – 15th September
1984
Coal is the cheapest
See us on Stand 38
KINGS HALL BELFAST
COAL ADVISORY SERVICE
8 CASTLE LANE,
BELFAST. Tel. 229444
36 CARLISLE ROAD,
LONDONDERRY.
Tel. 261245
54 CHURCH STREET,
PORTADOWN.
Tel. 334847
24 GREENVALE ST.,
BALLYMENA.
Tel. 2131
Win a Free
Solid fuel
Heating System
in THE POT OF GOLD

For more than sixty years the Ideal Home Exhibition has attracted hundreds of thousands of people to The King's Hall. This attractive cover of the catalogue for the 1984 event has a very strong message for the domestic consumer.

COMMERCE AND CONFERENCES *Chapter 6*

THE KING'S HALL AT BALMORAL is one of the best known Exhibition Centres in the United Kingdom and since 1935, when the Hall was commissioned for such purposes, it has attracted many hundreds of thousands of visitors and exhibitors keen to do business. One of the earliest and the longest-running ventures is the Ideal Home Exhibition which began in 1935 and in recent years has witnessed a significant rejuvenation. In the past 60 years other Exhibitions have come and gone, yet others have re-invented themselves or returned under different names and a number of newcomers have catered for the public's ever changing tastes.

For many years the United Kingdom and Europe have lagged behind the United States where Exhibitions are phenomenally big business, but people on this side of the Atlantic are catching up remarkably fast. In the past 25 years Exhibitions have increased five-fold, and The King's Hall remains the third largest provincial Exhibition Centre in the United Kingdom.

The Ideal Homes Exhibition was first held in the Ulster Hall in 1928, moving to The King's Hall in 1935, when it was called "The Ideal Homes Housing and Health Exhibition". The promoter was a Mr T Williamson of Glasgow and it was in 1936 that the Daniels family became the promoters. In 1935 The King's Hall rental was £500. It was nurtured successfully by the ebullient entrepreneur Herbert Daniels (and later by his son Bernard), and it reached its peak in the mid-Fifties when it could attract, on average, some 140,000 visitors. At its height some 40-50 Corporation buses were specially laid-on, and the customers from those years where known affectionately as "The Red Bus Brigade".

The Show House has always been the main feature of the Ideal Home Exhibition, and the 1994 version situated in the centre of The King's Hall was no exception. It takes about six weeks to build the house and it has to be demolished (and all debris removed) within three days!

The reasons for this success were complex, but they include the feeling of expansion and well-being after the stringencies and rationing of the Second World War. People were becoming better-off financially and more goods were available for purchasing. This was also the beginning of the end of the pre-television age when people were seeking spectacle and entertainment which was not available in their homes through the flick of a switch - though to describe television as essentially spectacle and entertainment is perhaps rather too kind to a medium which has been allowed to absorb and transmit a great many programmes that are merely tawdry and sensational.

In the Fifties, the world was still relatively innocent compared to the satiation and cynicism of today, and whole families flocked to the adventure of a night at The King's Hall Ideal Home Exhibition - which was run so astutely by the Daniels empire, with the proprietor travelling by Rolls Royce and sporting the inevitable and inevitably large cigar. Those were the days when the *Belfast Telegraph* was closely associated with the Ideal Home Exhibition, and the newspaper's "Mr Presents" and "Mr Password" were on hand to enhance the evening with a suitable prize, and to boost the newspaper's circulation in the process. Press barons, especially the original Lord (Roy) Thomson, were not in the business of giving away presents for nothing. Such calculated generosity unwittingly caused problems for young reporters, like this writer, who had the chore of interviewing prize-winners and writing up the story in such a way that it would entice people to buy a special edition of the Paper at the Show next evening in the hope of winning a prize.

Memories flood back of one middle-aged lady who had just won a washing machine. "What do you think of that?" asked the young reporter, who was hoping for a catchy reply to boost its story. There was a silence. Then the lady said "It's very nice." The reporter replied with just a hint of desperation "Anything more to say?" She replied "Not really". The reporter, faced with a blank notebook and an urgent deadline then said hoarsely "Missus are you saying that you came to the Exhibition to see the latest developments in homes and furnishings? Are you also saying that you are a regular reader of the *Belfast Telegraph* and that you are delighted to have won a brand new washing machine from "Mr Presents" and that you would recommend other readers to come to Balmoral, to see this great Show and to try to win a prize from this generous newspaper." Another pause, and she replied "Yes, something like that."

The reporter raced off to phone across his story, oblivious to any suggestion that he might have been putting one or two words in the mouth of a lady who had absolutely nothing to say for herself, even on winning a new washing machine! Reporters who won their spurs on such unpromising material in the years before the Troubles were well-equipped later on to take stories about bombs and bullets in their stride! The same could not be said of the Ideal Home Exhibition itself. Although it survived resolutely through the Troubles, like many another Northern Ireland institution, the organisers were forced to cancel the Exhibition in 1972 which was the most violent year in the Province's notably violent history over 25 years.

Despite the huge success of the Ideal Home Exhibition in those years, big changes were on the way and the older-style Exhibition had to compete with the rise of the huge-supermarkets which offered razor-keen prices and, equally significantly, accessible parking.

A whole generation had done well commercially in the halcyon days of the early Exhibitions but they had little idea how to market and sell such a huge project for the Eighties and Nineties. The Daniels family sold the franchise in 1981 to the Belfast firm of Joseph Robinson & Sons (Belfast) Ltd who had been involved in the Exhibition since 1975, as builders of the Show House in The King's Hall, and the Ideal Home Exhibition took a new direction and indeed a new lease of life. Those who know about such things would claim that the Ideal Home Exhibition has grown even stronger in the past 5–10 years. Part of the attraction is that people in this age of affluence (and Northern Ireland is affluent by world standards) are keen to sample the best in building and furnishings, and wish to keep up with the latest trends.

Some Shows in other parts of the United Kingdom have lost ground because they have become a mixture of trade fairs and a carnival with what insiders call 'barkers and grafters' (small-time businesses) being allowed space and stands to make up the numbers. This has not happened at Balmoral where the Ideal Home Exhibition has retained the central feature of one "Ideal Home" house, and sometimes more than one. More recently a major attraction has been the building of a house as the Exhibition progressed, so that people can watch the latest building techniques being applied before their very eyes. Such major attractions have been backed up by good service to customers, including a first-class creche, and stands offering goods and services of high quality. The background of the Exhibition visitor has also changed, with a predominance of better off people compared to their parents and grandparents from the Red Bus Brigade in the Fifties who had to depend on Belfast Corporation for their transport.

The Ideal Home Exhibition at Balmoral is one of the institutions of Northern Ireland which has survived with style through the changing decades and at this time of writing seems set for a long time to come. The number of visitors remains impressive, and in 1995 over 100,000 people went through the turnstiles. However, while the Ideal Home Exhibition remains the biggest public attraction in terms of numbers, there are others which bring significant numbers to The Kings' Hall. For example, the Ulster Motor Show has an attendance of some 60,000 in six days, Holiday World has 35,000 visitors over five days, whilst the annual Halloween indoor funfair – Funderland – attracts around 100,000 (young and old) during its seventeen-day season. In addition to these annual public events, there is a growing number of exhibitions which are trade-orientated, and although not attracting tens of thousands of visitors, they do have very significant attendances. These include the biennial Food & Drink (NIFEX) and Building Exhibitions and also the biannual Furniture Fairs. There are some Exhibitions, however, which fade away due to factors beyond the control of the organisers or the Royal Ulster – including, for example the Engineering and Materials Handling Exhibitions of the Seventies and Eighties which were badly hit by the recession in the building industry.

Other Exhibitions take on new forms. One example is the Boat Show which began in 1969, then became the Boats and Leisure Exhibition, then Hobbies and Holidays, then faded in the Eighties, and has returned in another dimension as Holiday World – with a new section on Camping and Caravanning. Exhibitors are constantly searching for new ways to attract the public, and a prototype "Mothers and Baby Show" in England three years ago, will appear in a different form at Balmoral as the "Parent and Child Exhibition". There is also great potential for the development of a Bridal Fair, given that there are some 10,000 weddings each year in Northern Ireland at an estimated average cost of £5,000 per wedding – which adds up to a great deal of money surrounding a major highlight in the lives of young (and not so young) couples and their families. Plans are also well in hand for an Environmental Exhibition and perhaps the resurrection of a business-to-business type Exhibition in a new form.

There have been significant developments in the volume and type of exhibition business since the early Seventies, and Philip Rees has been very closely involved. In his role as Commercial Director he is responsible for maximising the use of the Society's facilities, as well as the income which this generates. He says "The Exhibition business has been better and better. The traders and the public are keen to do business and one of our jobs is to bring to Belfast the major players to help them show off their wares. If you have a well-advertised and well-promoted Exhibition, and if you can attract the buyers and also the traders who present themselves well, then you have a perfect forum for sales. Northern Ireland, per capita, is the most successful Exhibition Centre in the United Kingdom, and the attendances at Balmoral – given our population base – are really phenomenal." Balmoral and The Kings' Hall are marketed nationally in their own right as an Exhibition Centre, in addition to their use during the Annual Agricultural Show, the flagship event of the RUAS.

In the past, and perhaps to some degree at present, there are the natural and healthy tensions between those members who believe that the RUAS is first and foremost an "Agricultural" Society with important commercial overtones, and those who believe that the considerable

The Ulster Motor Show was first staged in The King's Hall in 1970 and celebrated its Silver Jubilee in 1994. The event has since become biennial, but it still retains considerable popularity – with all the available indoor exhibition facilities transformed into a massive car showroom, as this photograph of the 1991 event demonstrates.

income generated by the commercial activities ensure the survival of the "Agricultural" priority of the Society's work. While the Agricultural work of the Society is paramount, the members are fortunate in having such a commercial back-up to help maintain the overall business in a hard-headed world where sentiment and tradition do not pay the rent.

The 1981 Ulster Motor Show catalogue featured the Dunmurry built De Lorean sports car on its cover. The car attracted considerable attention on its debut at the show but regrettably the hopes for the distinctive gull-wing vehicle never materialised.

The King's Hall is also well-known for its contribution to entertainment, and this aspect is covered in detail in the next Chapter. This provides an important dimension to the life of The King's Hall. The resurgence of popular entertainment at Balmoral relates back to several key concerts in the Seventies. After the Beatles came in the mid-Sixties, there was a huge drop-off until the mid-Seventies. This was partly due to the Troubles, when major outside entertainers were unwilling to come to Northern Ireland. However an approach was made in 1976 by the local promoter Jim Aiken, and as a result Demis Roussos, who was a big man in every way, played to a capacity audience in The King's Hall. He was followed by Nana Mouskouri, and these concerts were a big break-through for local audiences who had been starved of front-line international entertainers. From 1976 there was a steady build-up of concerts, and this

continued through the 1980s when the number of concerts per year started to decline, and the demand increased for use of the Complex for Exhibitions. As Philip Rees remarks: "There have been fewer concerts partly because there has been a recent dearth of top-line stars who are more than one month or one-year wonders, apart from regular visitors like Sir Cliff Richard who is absolutely phenomenal. Another problem is that the Exhibition work is so successful that we have less time and space for concerts. Our best year was 1989 when we had 23 concert days and two world boxing championship contests."

(Above) The King's Hall Complex is no place for the faint-hearted when 'Funderland' is held each year at Halloween. The big wheel, taller than The King's Hall itself, provides a colourful entree to the indoor funfair. (Photograph: Chris Hill)

(Right) Sir Cliff Richard has been a regular performer in The King's Hall for many years. This photograph was taken in 1962 when he appeared with The Shadows. The show was staged by Philip Raymond Solomon and local acts also appearing on the programme included Rodney Foster and his Jazzmen, Elaine and Derek and Walter Davison and the Melotones.

Balmoral is big business, in more ways than one. In 1961, it added yet another dimension when the Central Exhibition Hall (renamed The Balmoral Hall following its recent refurbishment) was leased for 10 months each year to the BBC for its television production facilities. Many well-known programmes were produced there including those featuring the late, lamented James Young and the dreadful and unlamented failure called "The Show" which must have been one of the most expensive disasters in the history of the BBC in Northern Ireland. Balmoral was used by the BBC for some 30 years until the development of its own large Blackstaff studios based in Belfast.

Another important commercial outlet is the Balmoral Conference Centre which early in 1995 was given a major boost in the British Isles when it was used by the Prime Minister of the United Kingdom John Major and the Irish Prime Minister John Bruton to launch the so-called Framework Documents to try to establish lasting peace in Northern Ireland. Though the Conference Centre was ideal geographically for two Premiers who wanted to meet halfway on this island, literally and symbolically, it was a neat irony that Balmoral was chosen as the venue. The young men who had marched past Sir Edward Carson at Balmoral in 1912, and who subsequently had fought at the Somme in 1916, would have blinked at the very idea of an "Irish" Prime Minister, and swallowed hard at the thought of a meeting with the British Prime Minister – at Balmoral, of all places.

There is no doubt, however, that the widespread television coverage of this event made some commercial sense for the Centre which shortly afterwards hosted another important political figure – the President of the European Commission Jacques Santer. The Balmoral Conference Centre began life as the Members' Rooms and the ET Green Hall which were opened in 1965. Though impressive at the outset, within two decades it looked a little dated in a business where people were demanding a standard of accommodation that was more than the efficient but clinical ambience which Balmoral offered. Some limited refurbishment took place in the Eighties, but the Society faced the major challenge in the Nineties and spent £500,000 in bringing the facilities to a high standard.

The "ET Green Hall", a term that did not trip off the tongue, was re-named "The Octagon" and the Members' Rooms were restyled into the Balmoral Conference Centre, though in a happy compromise they are known as "The Members' Rooms" for the duration of the Show. With a concerted marketing campaign, bookings have increased considerably in recent years, and new dimensions are being added all the time. In 1994 the Octagon was used most successfully by the Belfast Festival at Queen's to stage the British Telecom "Supper Club" with Fascinating Aida, and plans are in hand to enhance what may become an annual event. In today's competitive business world, the Balmoral Conference Centre offers good self-contained facilities with excellent parking and comprehensive security. And it is all part of a complex commercial operation to ensure that the RUAS remains solvent and able to fulfil its prime objective of promoting all that is good about the Northern Ireland Agri-Food industry.

(Above) Balmoral was featured worldwide on 22 February 1995 when Prime Minister John Major and Irish Premier John Bruton launched the key "Frameworks for the Future" document. Over 400 members of the World's media were present to cover the launch, and relayed their stories from the hastily-prepared press office and television studios which were set up within The King's Hall Complex.

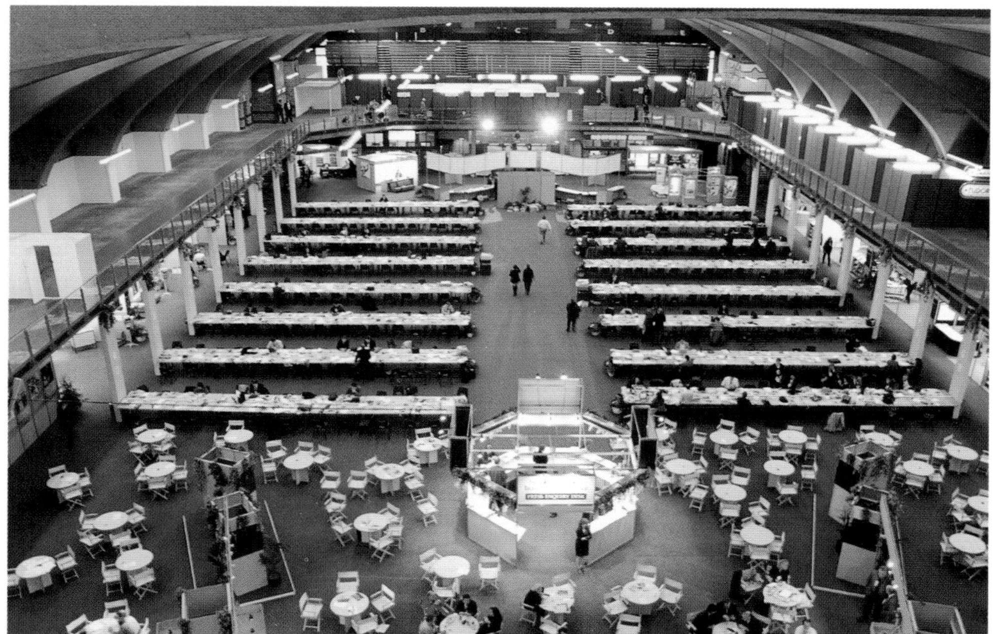

(Left) Further world-wide coverage was given to The King's Hall Complex during the visit of President Bill Clinton to Northern Ireland in November 1995 when the Complex was transformed into an International Press Centre.

The first boxing tournament in The King's Hall – the night the lights went out! The 10,000 spectators wait patiently for the Warnock/Huguenin championship fight in November 1934, little knowing of the controversy that was to follow.

A STAGE FOR ALL THE WORLD *Chapter 7*

THE MAIN OBJECTIVE OF THE MEMBERS of the Royal Ulster Agricultural Society and their forebears was always to provide a setting for the exhibition of the best of livestock and farming practice, and also to display the latest agricultural and other relevant machinery for the benefit of the farming community. This was, and remains, the priority of the Society. Yet, over the years, the name of Balmoral has become synonymous with a vast array of non-agricultural activities which, in addition to the various exhibitions already referred to in the previous Chapter, include entertainments (ranging from Mantovani to the Beatles), sports (ranging from rugby football to boxing) and rallies of religious, political and national significance.

A search through the Society's archives uncovers a remarkable list of people who took the centre stage at The King's Hall, from dynamic preachers to dance-band leaders and world-champion boxers to Louis Armstrong and his All-Stars. From the earliest days, there was evidence of non-agricultural entertainment at Balmoral, with one of the first Shows offering a sharp-shooting competition for those who had a penchant for a "bull's-eye" of a different kind. In the Minutes of the Works Committee in May 1904 it was stated that "The use of the grounds was offered to Buffalo Bill's Wild West Co Ltd, for fourteen days in September, and for the sum of £250." It was also noted, however, that the company subsequently decided not to visit Ireland that year.

In 1912 Balmoral was the venue for a high-profile Exhibition of aircraft manoeuvres which ended in disaster with the tragic death of one of the airmen, a Mr HJD Astley.[1] During this period it was also a stage of another kind when in the run-up to the Home Rule Crisis prior

The Society lost no time in utilising the new King's Hall. This indoor tennis exhibition in June 1939 proved to be a major crowd attraction.

to the First World War, the Young Citizen Volunteers paraded at Balmoral and were reviewed by Sir Edward Carson.

During the First World War the Balmoral premises were closed to the public. However the Society regained its momentum after the War and it became clear to its leading officials that the Society, and Northern Ireland, needed a large community venue to equal that of Olympia or the Kelvin Hall in Glasgow. This was the thinking which led to the evolution and opening of The King's Hall in 1934.[2]

When it was completed, the Society lost no time in utilizing its new premises, and the long list of programme publications gives an impressive account of the sheer range of activities in and around this vast Arena and Showgrounds – in October 1934 they staged the Belfast Radio Exhibition (the first non-agricultural commercial event in The King's Hall), in May 1935 the Jubilee Celebrations of the Ulster Youth Organisations, in November that year an Ulster Boy Scouts Bazaar, in July 1937 the Coronation celebrations, and in June 1939 a Tennis Exhibition.

These, in fact, are only a fraction of the many events which took place at Balmoral during those years, but no report would be complete without references to The King's Hall as a venue for International Boxing and Wrestling. The King's Hall has been associated with the names of outstanding world champions, ranging from Rinty Monaghan to Barry McGuigan, and those who have attended such sporting extravaganzas will always remember that cauldron of noise and excitement, as well as the blood and violence, of a big Boxing night in Belfast. One man who remembers more than most is Jack Magowan, who for nearly 45 years, was the

Boxing Correspondent for the *Belfast Telegraph* and the marvellously titled *Ireland's Saturday Night*. He recalls some of the main highlights.

> They still talk about the night the lights went out in The King's Hall. Jimmy Warnock, his eyes saucersize in a sallow face, had been floored by a peach of a right hook from the Frenchman, Maurice Huguenin, and he looked in terrible trouble. "Two . . . three . . . four . . ." tolled the referee as Ireland's boxing legend struggled bravely to regain his feet. "Five . . . six . . . seven . . ."
>
> Then, suddenly, all hell broke loose. Somebody had pulled a switch controlling the lighting system and the arena was in darkness! Nobody could see a thing, least of all the two fighters as they stumbled over one another in an impromptu version of "Blind Man's Buff". Warnock never forgot the night he won a contest he should have lost.
>
> It was about a month before Christmas 1935, the first time a spanking new King's Hall had opened its doors to International boxing. All fight nights in those pre-War days had the glamour and excitement of a Linfield-Celtic Cup tie, and bookmaker Jim Rice knew he had backed a winner. "This was the biggest indoor stadium in Ireland, and the crowd was fantastic," recalled Rice years later. "Some people queued all day only to find their seats already taken. It was bedlam. The stewards were powerless to control the mob and Warnock had a real struggle getting from his dressing-room to the ring."
>
> Imagine the look of shocked disbelief on a sea of faces when their hero hit the deck from that Huguenin haymaker. It was as though the roof of the arena had fallen in. As a man, 10,000 startled fans rose to their feet, the overture to a sequence of events that were to make boxing history and spark off years of controversy.
>
> It was late in round two that Warnock's match-stick legs were swept from under him. The referee took up the count. "Get up . . . get up," screamed Jimmy's backers in the corner, hammering frantic fists on the apron of the ring. The dazed fighter just shook his head. Was he hearing their pleas above the noise and panic? Suddenly, everything went black. Like a snuffed out candle, the huge arc-lamp above the ring seemed to short circuit, plunging the stadium into darkness. The crowd cheered, jeered, whistled and cat-called derisively. Somebody lit a firework that didn't go off. The place was in an uproar. It was several minutes before the lighting was restored, and by then Warnock was back on his corner stool, his head wrapped in a wet towel. Had Jimmy been saved from a knock-out? The question has been asked a thousand times. Nobody will ever know!
>
> If the ghost of Jimmy Warnock lives on, so do rich and vivid memories of a rewarding era in Irish boxing – The King's Hall era. The brave, sometimes

Chief Executive Bill Yarr recalls travelling with his father by tram to Balmoral for this defence of Rinty Monaghan's World flyweight title. He still has the ringside ticket which cost £3. A similar seat at one of today's world Championship fights would cost fifty times this amount.

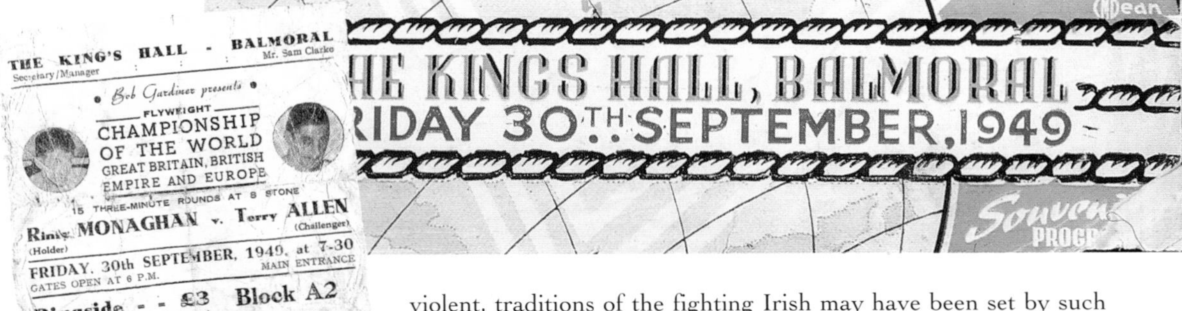

violent, traditions of the fighting Irish may have been set by such bare-fisted braggarts as Dan Donnelly and the hot-tempered Peter Corcoran over 200 years ago, but nothing has changed. Only the venues in which battle has been waged, and top among them has always been that Coliseum of brass-knuckled action at Balmoral.

To Rinty Monaghan, The King's Hall was "Belfast's own private thrill factory," and all major shows there generate an atmosphere and fervour probably unique in sport. "The place becomes radio-active," wrote that doyen of boxing writers,

Nat Fleischer, after a charged-up baptism in Monaghan's day. "The noise is like thunder. Mix in Irish emotions and excitability, plus the thrills of a good fight, and you have the most potent of all boxing cocktails outside Mexico or the Caribbean." Fleischer might have had Warnock v Lynch in mind, or Gilroy v Caldwell, maybe even Bassa v McAuley Mark 1. All three contests ascended to a special place in boxing history, and made somebody a great deal of money.

Not Warnock, I hasten to add. He was paid only £190 for winning a 12-rounder against the then World flyweight champion, Benny Lynch, a record purse then for an Ulster boxer. Alas, at today's exchange rates, Jimmy would be richer by nearly £100,000! Nor did Spider Kelly, from Londonderry, fare much better financially when he beat Caplan for the vacant British 9-stone title a few years later in 1938. They were exhilarating times for boxing in the Province and The King's Hall always seemed to be playing a virtuoso role. Like it did, too, for Rinty Monaghan when boxing glory, and a World crown, finally came his way.

It was in the spring of 1948 and there wasn't a dry eye in the Monaghan dressing-room after the drama of a seventh-round knock-out win over Jackie Paterson. As usual, Rinty treated the crowd to a song, but not with a chorus of "When Irish Eyes are Smiling". Instead, he chose "Broken Hearted Clown," something he was soon to regret. "It was thoughtless of me," this likeable little man confessed later. "I never realised how badly it hurt Paterson's feelings, and I'm genuinely sorry!"

Like Monaghan, Freddie Gilroy was the purest of fighters. He never lost a contest in The King's Hall, and the explosion of pride and hysteria that crowned his victory over Johnny Caldwell must have been heard at Shaftesbury Square. There were 10,000 fans through the turnstiles for this one, not as many as for Cohen v John Kelly eight years before, but as close to an all-time high as made no difference. The rumpus that greeted Charlie Hill's hotly disputed win over Billy Kelly was yesterday's news – happily, this is the only occasion in which

Barry McGuigan's fights in the mid-1980's created the most amazing atmosphere in The King's Hall. In recognition of his successes and the spin-off in terms of worldwide publicity for Balmoral, Council made Barry an honorary member of the Society. In return, the Chief Executive received this autographed photograph.

> crowd trouble has left a bad taste after a King's Hall show – but it would be nearly 20 years after Gilroy before a country-boy from Monaghan came on the scene, giving a floundering sport a new and captive audience.
>
> Barry McGuigan topped seven Barney Eastwood King's Hall bills in all, every one of them a sell-out, and for two years in the mid-80's he was arguably the most watchable sportsman in Ireland. To hero-hungry Ulster fans, the "Clones Cyclone" was more than just a winner. He was Hercules, Ivanhoe and D'Artagnan rolled into one, the lad with a 100 kilowatt smile and the talent to match.
>
> McGuigan at his best was awesome, a superb boxer-puncher. His Oscar-winning contest with the tough Puerto Rican, Juan Laporte, was a classic, probably the best 10-round fight ever seen in The King's Hall. A McGuigan night at Balmoral had a magical quality rarely felt in sport. His reign as a World Champion, and boxing's hottest property, was all too brief. What some of us wouldn't give to turn back the clock, back to the time when they hung from the rafters (almost) in salute to an athlete who brought honour to himself and a troubled Province. His like are not often seen, or found again!

In stark contrast to the blood and thunder of boxing, so vividly recalled by Jack Magowan, The King's Hall has frequently been the venue for the fervour of a religious crusade. In June 1975, the Editor of the *Belfast Telegraph*, Roy Lilley, sent his fresh-faced Chief Features Writer (a certain Alf McCreary) to produce a word-picture of a crusade by an American Evangelist Dr John E Haggai. He wrote as follows:

> Belfast on a humid summer evening. Hundreds of people threading their way to The King's Hall in their Sunday best. The neat lines, sensible clothes and well-scrubbed faces of the Ulster faithful and faithless who have come to hear the American evangelist Dr John E Haggai. The huge hall is well-filled. One of the stewards estimates the audience at 4,000. A pop star or a politician would be flattered. There is a hum of expectation. Hymnbooks and leaflets on every seat. At the front a huge choir in angelic white basks under the hot auditorium lights. And lording over all, a massive sign in red lettering "Christ Is The Answer".
>
> On the dot of 8.00 pm Mr Don De Vos swings the choir into praise. Hymn 33, for everyone, choir and audience: "We have heard the joyful sound, Jesus saves . . ." Then another less well-known hymn. Subdued singing. "We'll turn to Number 38," says Don De Vos. "When the roll is called up yonder. Do you know it?" Massive assent. We all roar into the chorus. It is difficult to take notes and sing. "When the roll is called" at the same time, but I am there.
>
> The atmosphere starts for lift-off. There is a growing togetherness in the warmth of the music. Why, indeed, should the Devil have all the best tunes? Then the soloist, a trendy-looking Jim Kearce who, clearly, was a hit with the

choir, sings "Put your hand in the hand of the man who stilled the waters." From the back of the Hall he seemed slightly remote. The acoustics in the cavernous building are not good.

We are swinging along. Not many obvious sinners about. One of the things about sin is that you cannot spot the sinners. I wonder how many people at this Crusade would eat you alive politically in the narrowness of Ulster. Then the leader talks about tangible results for all eternity. And the tangible results for the night are put in little brown envelopes and collected in white plastic buckets. There is no pressure about giving, no hard-sell financially.

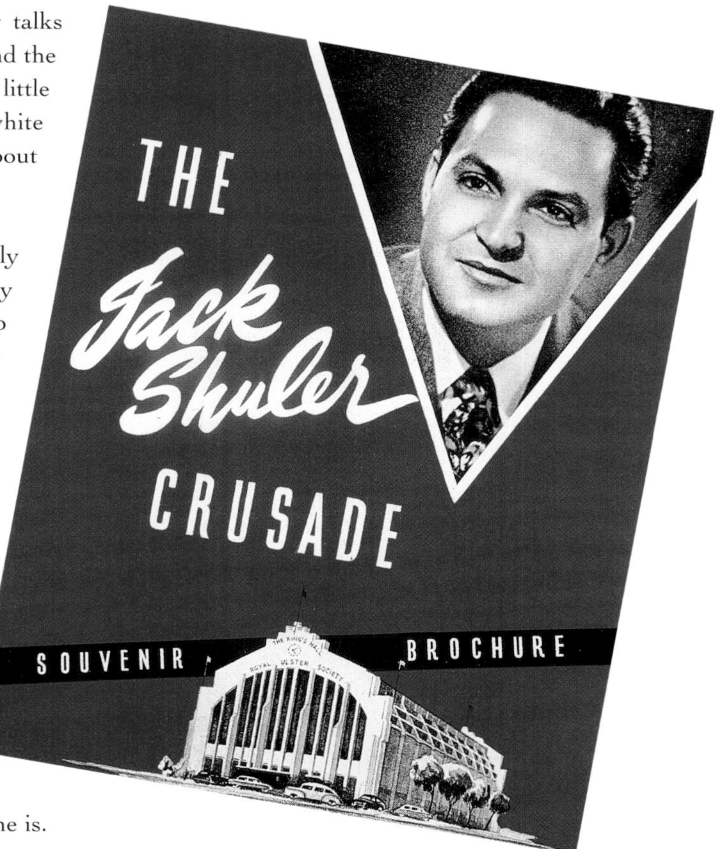

I discover to my horror that I have only two coins and no notes, apart from strictly professional jottings. I slip the coins into the envelope and make a mental note to give a bit more to the usual charities next week. Then the choir, in the words of Don De Vos, "will rise and shine." They do. The Hymnbooks are collected by stewards, some of them female. Stanzas of Amazing Grace obscure all earthly thoughts of stylish lines.

At 8.30 Dr John Haggai takes the rostrum. It is a quiet entrance, even an anti-climax. No build-up, no announcement, he arrives as if assuming that everyone will know who he is.

From a distance Haggai looks stocky, a little swarthy, compact. He moves swiftly, takes the microphone, says a prayer. He announces the following night's subjects. On Saturday the theme will be "Where are the Dead?" Then he turns to the night's question: "Can we have assurance of salvation?" He speaks quickly, staccato, moving about the rostrum, punching the air with a finger to underline his points, a man with presence, confidence, and a strong preaching style. Like every evangelist I have heard from Belfast through Glasgow to Edmonton in Canada and back, he rattles through the Scriptures at a furious pace, throwing out references and cross-references: which assumes, to my mind, that he is in danger of preaching to the converted. What about the man who does not read the Bible? Dr Haggai constructs his address well, but he leaves little time for his many points to sink in.

Dr John Haggai was not the only evangelist to hold a Crusade in The King's Hall. Jack Shuler, one of America's most gifted and elequent preachers and a close friend of Dr Billy Graham, attracted full houses of 7,500 to each of his services, held daily over a two-week period in 1955.

Religion is a serious matter, and I would be the first to concur. But I note that John Haggai gets his first light chuckle from the audience after 20 minutes. Some other speakers tend to identify with the audience in this way much earlier on.

Then like a high-strata jet plane that homes to base on cue, Dr Haggai comes to one crucial point: "What is the relationship between God and you, is it the right relationship, have you committed yourself to Christ, or is it merely head knowledge?" Then Dr Haggai asks those who want that "right relationship" to put up their hand. Don De Vos helps him to count the hands. "Thank you over there, there's another little girl, God bless you, you and you, yes, over there. . ." In little bursts of one or two the hands shoot up.

Then as the choir sings softly in the background Dr Haggai invites those who have put up their hands to come to the front. Even in public this is essentially a very private moment. You tend to avert the eyes from a direct stare as these people make their personal decisions. Haggai helps. "This is it, you are on the threshold, come right now, you are making this decision, right now." But Haggai does it in a quiet way. Again there is no hard sell. It is just a voice helping some out of the wilderness of personal doubt.

Those who have come forward are led away to another room for private discussions with trained counsellors. I count 66 faces on the way out, some of them counsellors, and some of them young children. I think this a poor response, but a counsellor assures me afterwards that it is satisfactory. He says a Crusade often starts slowly. This one is lasting for three weeks, and people often take some time to make up their minds.

After the converts leave I look up to the stage. It is precisely 9.10. Dr John Haggai has gone. There is no final hymn. The meeting breaks up with an air of anti-climax. Some people sit listening to the choir rehearsing. Others file towards the doors. I register a feeling of slight disappointment that the mood has been allowed to evaporate into The King's Hall air.

On the way out I ponder on the difficulties facing a man like John Haggai. It cannot be easy to present the Christian challenge every night in such a way. I tell myself that the Crusade would benefit from better stage-management. There are still many loose ends. As I walk through the deserted Balmoral Showgrounds with darkness falling early for June, I am trying to place the quotation: "Judge not that ye be not judged." I trust that there is salvation for reporters too.

There was indeed salvation for reporters, and the writer received a kind note from Dr Haggai a few days later!

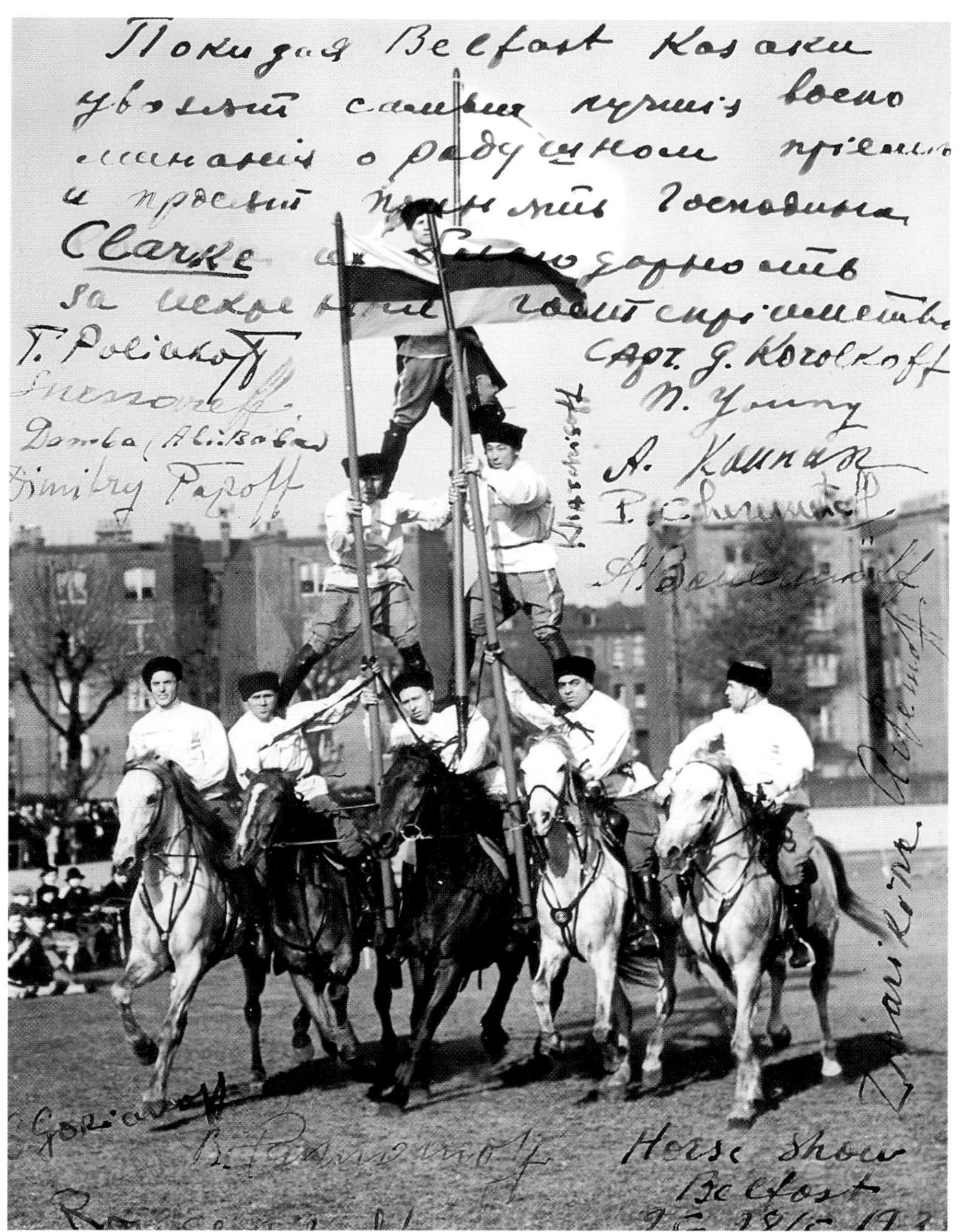

The Cossacks appeared at the 1938 Annual Show and this autographed photograph of the occasion is a prized possession in the Society's archives.

Entertainment at Balmoral was associated with the Showground arena as well as The King's Hall. Featured as major attractions at Balmoral Show, there were numerous military displays, free-fall parachutists, 'death-defying' motor cyclists who drove through rings of fire, skilled horsemen including the famous Cossacks and the Royal Canadian Mounted Police. Each in their own way and at their own time thrilled generations of Show patrons and maintained Balmoral's reputation for good entertainment on the "Big Day Out," though often the quality and the entertainment in the Showgrounds was all too dependent on the weather.

It is not generally realised that Balmoral was at one time a well-known centre for sport, apart from boxing and wrestling. In the early days, genteel cycling was allowed in the Showgrounds. On 8 May 1897, the Council passed a resolution that they would admit ladies to the use of the cycling track on Mondays, Wednesdays and Fridays. There is no record of what happened on the other days. Later the premises were used for other sports, and notably rugby. After Show Jumping which was a major attraction at the 1896 Show (about which more is described in the next Chapter), Rugby Football was the first sport to make a real impact at Balmoral with the area inside the trotting track at the main enclosure being ideal for the game. Between 1898 and 1921 it was the venue for eleven Internationals featuring Ireland against Wales, Scotland and South Africa. In only four of these games were the home team victorious.

Rugby Internationals at Balmoral during the early part of the century gave the Belfast public the opportunity to watch top-class football. The game between Ireland and South Africa in November 1906 was no exception, with the visitors winning 15 – 12. The line up of the teams behind the Arena Grandstands is interesting in that the corrugated fence in the background still stands today, ninety years later! (Photograph: The Tedford Scrapbook, I.R.F.U)

In 1902, Scotland were beaten whilst Wales lost in 1904, 1906 and 1912. The 1906 Irish victory was memorable with the legendary Alfie Tedford, a short burly figure of abnormal strength with long arms and a powerful hand-off, scoring, by all accounts, two wonderful tries. Ireland won 11-6, despite having both half-backs sitting injured on the touch line.

Alfie Tedford was no stranger to Balmoral, for he was a member of the Malone Club whose home was at the Showgrounds. Malone took up residence in 1903 at a rent of £30 per annum. In 1907 the Society suggested that an increase to £40 was appropriate. The history of Malone RFC (celebrating its centenary in 1992) states: "A compromise was reached at £35 and the Secretary of the RUAS was made an Honorary Member!"

International rugby disappeared from Balmoral when Ravenhill was opened in 1925, and Malone moved on to their present home at Gibson Park in 1935 and although there were a number of junior matches played in the late Forties and Fifties, this effectively finished the rugby era at the Showgrounds. Some people claim that this was due to the opposition of the Horse Committee who objected to the grounds being used for such events. The Annual Report of 1935, however, provides strong evidence that financial considerations were the real reason for the demise of rugby and other sports at Balmoral. A Minute from the Finance Committee Report states: "A substantial payment had to be made in respect of city rates in which the main charge was made in connection with The Kings Hall and unfortunately the Society which was formerly exempt will have to continue to pay heavy rates. The arrangement made with the authorities has involved the cessation of all lettings as such of grounds and premises which now must be used exclusively for the Society's Show. The Council greatly regrets that

Royal Ulster Constabulary Athletic Tournament
June, 1933

The RUC Sports always attracted top-class athletes from the UK and beyond. This sprint race at the 1933 Games was watched by a capacity Arena crowd.

necessity has compelled the Society to cease the use of the grounds for Athletic sports, rugby, football, hockey and events other than those relating to its own work. This opportunity was taken to record thanks to Malone Rugby Football Club, the RUC Athletic Association, Victoria College and the Ulsterville Harrier Athletics Association from whom useful revenue has been derived."

However, it was not the end of the road – or the end of the track – for the RUC Athletic Association. The Annual RUC Sports had been a regular feature in the Arena since 1930, and because it was a one-off event during the year rather than an agreement for the use of facilities throughout the year, the rating problem did not arise. The event continued to thrive with large crowds attracted by the presence of top-rate athletes from UK and beyond. Many Commonwealth and Olympic champions enthralled spectators, with performers such as Kenyan sprint champion Seraphae Antio, high jumper Prince Adedoyin of Nigeria, the famous 1948 Jamaican relay team of Herb McKinley, Arthur Wint, George Roden and Leslie Lang and, of course, our own Thelma Hopkins and Mary Peters.

Agricultural Showgrounds throughout the United Kingdom are greatly favoured as suitable venues for Dog Shows and Balmoral is no exception. Whether those events are "sport", "entertainment" or something else is a matter of opinion, but it is certain that the Belfast Dog Show Society is the oldest tenant of the Showgrounds. The first Belfast Dog Show at Balmoral was held in 1924, and apart from an enforced break during the Second World War the event has been held annually since then. It is held at the end of September, as a qualifier for Crufts, and attracts dog-fanciers and their pets from all over the UK.

A second significant Dog Show, held on Easter Tuesday, almost matches the longevity of the September event, having been started in the early 1930s by the Ulster Fox Terrier Club.

Dog Shows have been a feature of the Balmoral calendar for over seventy years. These two happy ladies exhibited what they hoped would be "Best of Breed".

The Hallé Orchestra visited Belfast in August 1946 when for three nights in succession, it attracted to its concerts the largest audiences for Symphony Concerts ever assembled in Northern Ireland. When the concert series was announced it was generally felt that it was a daring experiment. However, these fears were unfounded, and the concerts were a great success with the Orchestra inspired by their famous conductor Sir John Barbarolli (right). As a result of this success, the Halle made a return visit to The King's Hall in September 1947.

The King's Hall itself could be relied upon to provide entertainment for all seasons, whether it be a jazz concert with the Ted Heath Orchestra and Winifred Atwell in 1950, a concert in 1947 by the Liverpool Philharmonic Orchestra, and the Halle Orchestra under its world-renowned Conductor Sir John Barbarolli. There were many other famous names including Gracie Fields, Mario Lanza, and, for succeeding generations, the ageless Sir Cliff Richard. The quality of these promotions varied – the Louis Armstrong All Stars were not well served by the accoustics in 1962, but those who have attended the concerts of Cliff Richard and others will have marvelled at the sheer professionalism of the presentation of their shows in such a huge auditorium.

The King's Hall circus was always popular and the 1949 Christmas production included six elephants, six lions, five tigers, a "famous Arab troupe of whirling acrobats", and the original singing cowboy from the Rockies (perhaps an early Glen Campbell!) as well as "Hurricane bare-back riders" and "the untameable mule".

The King's Hall was famous for ice-skating, from 1939 to 1969. Sadly, the onset of the Troubles meant that The King's Hall was requisitioned by the security forces and this brought a wonderful era to an end. Many people to this day retain vivid memories of an evening on the rink – including this writer who could not stand up in his skates and consequently has admired the genius of world-class skaters like Torvill and Dean who, appropriately, included The King's Hall on their farewell professional tour in 1995, during which they even brought their own ice-rink.

For all sorts of reasons, all sorts of people from Northern Ireland and beyond have all kinds of happy memories of nights of entertainment at The King's Hall which has been one of the great venues on this island for so many years. The vision of those who conceived and built The King's Hall away back in the early Thirties has been justified many times over. They would be proud to know that the "momentous step" they took more than 60 years ago is still paying rich dividends for the people of Northern Ireland and countless visitors too.

THE KING'S HALL
ICE RINK
FOR THREE DAYS
Thursday, Friday, Saturday, 20th, 21st, 22nd October
EACH EVENING AT 7.30 O'CLOCK
JOHN PEARSON Presents
HIS FIRST KING'S HALL SHOW

★ ICELANDIA ★

An International All-Star Skating Spectacle
BRILLIANT - - - THRILLING - - - SENSATIONAL

VALERIE MOON
Runner-up to Cecilia Colledge in the British Open Professional Championship.

BILL & JULIE BARRETT
British Ice Dance Championship Runners-up, 1949.

MISS DAGMAR LERCHOVA
(Czechoslovakia). Universities Champion of the World.

BRIDGET SHIRLEY ADAMS
Britain's Famous Olympic Games Representative.

GORDON HOLLOWAY
British Junior Figure Skating Championship Runner-up, 1949.

WEMBLEY ICE DANCE ENSEMBLE
In Spectacular Formation Sequences Featuring:—
Gladys Kollicker, Margaret Brookes, Joyce Desmet, Pat Garraway, Moira Crook, Anne Cooper, Fred Bubb, Gerry Gaskell, Alan Webb, Len Attwood, Charles Wood, Bob Cooper

SHIRLEY BURKE
Belfast's Own Gold Medallist Star who has Twice been Third in the British Open Professional Championship.

DIANA GRAFTON
In her Celebrated Rhythm Number—Direct from the United States.

JOE WHITEHOUSE
The Daring Stilt Skater.

JACK McCONNELL
The Scottish Ice Comedian.

HAROLD BETTS & HIS ORCHESTRA
The Show Devised and Compered by HOWARD BASS

ADMISSION—Reserved Seats, 7/6 and 5/-. Unreserved Seats, 2/6.
All Prices include SKATING after Performances.

Seats Bookable from Noon, Monday 17th, at Ice Skating Rink Booking Office, Messrs. Leslie Porter Ltd., 30, Great Victoria Street (opposite Opera House).

DAILY SKATING SESSIONS commence FRIDAY, 21st OCTOBER.

The 'Ice Era' at Balmoral encapsulated a period of thirty years from 1939. Many thousands of people experienced the thrill of individual skating on The King's Hall Rink or the excitement of watching ice hockey or one of the regular ice spectaculars held at this venue. This advertisement for John Pearson's first such show in October 1949 illustrates the wide range of artistes who came to Belfast for the event.

Memories of the old ice-skating days were revived in January 1995 when the world-famous Torvill & Dean enthralled over 30,000 spectators during their week long "Face the Music" – Farewell Spectacular Tour, during which they provided their own ice-rink!.

NOTES

1 Mentioned in Chapter Two.

2 Discussed in detail in Chapter Three.

This 1927 photograph shows a traditional method of schooling ponies with walking sticks.

"UP AND OVER" *Chapter 8*

THE BALMORAL SHOW HAS A WIDE VARIETY OF EVENTS AND ATTRACTIONS which, taken as a whole, give it a particular style and ethos. In another sense, however, it is an amalgamation of individual attractions, each with its own history, rules, participants and audiences – whether this be in the judging rings, the exhibition halls or indeed in the camaraderie of the restaurants and watering places. From the early days, however, one of the great attractions has been the Show Jumping which has not only maintained the high standards of Balmoral in general but also provided the opportunity to make new friends and to renew old acquaintances and rivalries in the cutting edge of competition.

The Show Jumping was a major attraction in the first Show held at Balmoral in June 1896, which despite the poor weather, was judged a great success. The events were reported by the Press in immense detail, and the indefatigable reporter for the *Northern Whig* provided an eye-witness account of the second day's proceedings in a style that was all his own:

> The horse jumping exhibition at three o'clock was honoured by the presence of Vice-Admiral Lord Walter Kerr and Rear-Admiral Powlet, who, with several officers of the Channel Fleet, lunched with Mr Musgrave, DL, before coming to the Show. The distinguished officers met with a very cordial welcome when recognised by the visitors in the ground. Stationed in the enclosure near the Grand Stand was the fine band of the Royal Irish Constabulary, which performed under the able conductorship of Mr Van Maanen.

At three o'clock the jumping commenced. By this time the reserved and unreserved portions of the enclosure were well filled, and there could not have been less than four or five thousand people present. The want of more extensive covered stand accommodation was soon severely felt, for the heavens, which had been extra lowering and black for some time, opened out with a vengeance before the first competition was half through, and the downpour which followed quite destroyed, to those who had no cover, the attractiveness of the show. It is not very easy to develop enthusiasm in even the most finished "lepper's" performance when the water is running in a stream down your neck from your neighbour's umbrella, while at the same time each drop that strikes you at an angle below the gingham enhances the growing dampness about your legs.

Happy were those six or seven hundred early birds who had monopolised the accommodation of the stand. Still, as showing how wonderfully these horse displays catch on with the public, it was gratifying to note the nine out of every ten of the "outlanders" bravely held their ground to the bitter end. As though in recognition of their pluck and sportsmanlike spirit, the rainclouds quite suddenly and unexpectedly lifted (after a good three-quarters of an hour's "pelt", the deluge ceased) and during the remainder of the proceedings there was no further pluvial visitation. The first competition, in which £50 of prize money was offered, was for hunters in classes 22 and 23 of the show.

Of seventy-one horses entered in these classes seventeen turned out for the jumping, but these included most of our best Northern performers. Messrs N Morton, Ballymena, and S Bailie, Newtownards, both held strong hands, Mr Morton particularly so with Little John (last year's Dublin winner), Poor Mary Ann, Twist, and Duke of Wellington. Mr Bailie relied upon those two sterling good animals Meta and Idalia. The course consisted of bank and ditch, double bank, stone wall, and water, and though only temporary erections they had been built well and carefully. Owing to the heavy rain of the previous night and early morning the going on the unfinished surface was terribly greasy even at starting, but after the big downpour, already referred to, it grew of course far worse, and some of the best performers under the circumstances failed to do themselves justice. When properly levelled and relaid (as it will be before next show) and the fences permanently established, the jumping ground will be a really splendid one, and, as it is thoroughly drained over its entire area, it will when it possesses a good sod on top give good going in any weather.

To return to the competition. It soon became evident that the great fight would be between Morton and Bailie. The latter good sportsman, however, was unlucky, for Meta was not on her best behaviour, while Idalia blundered a bit in the first round, though she afterwards performed well, and, as she was going great guns in the third essay – so much so as to elicit a hearty cheer from a by no means demonstrative crowd – many people thought she would attract the

> attention of the judge, but she did not, and in the end Mr Morton was awarded both first and second premiums for Little John and Poor Mary Ann, while Mr RL Calwell gained third for Canary. Little John displayed all his old steadiness and cleverness in negotiating his fences, and certainly deserved his place, but Poor Mary Ann, like Idalia, made a mistake in her first round.

And on and on and on . . . However, the *Northern Whig* reporter, in the midst of his descriptive canter, made some telling points, namely that the Show Jumping was popular and that the Balmoral facilities when properly upgraded could provide a first-class venue for the sport. And so it has proved, down the years. A modern reporter with a much greater economy of words and wide knowledge of his subject is Michael Slavin who traces the development of Show Jumping in Ireland and at Balmoral in particular.

> Ireland is given credit for having invented the sport of Show Jumping, and Balmoral has been part of its evolution on this island for up to 100 years. According to the Guinness Book of Show Jumping, compiled in 1987, by top British equestrian journalist Judith Draper, the first recorded official horse jumping events were held at the Royal Dublin Society in 1864 where horse and rider performed what were called HIGH JUMP and WIDE LEAP as part of a test for potential hunters and cavalry mounts. Gradually the number of fixed obstacles were increased to 10 on a given course. They included a gate, a water jump, banks, stone wall, stile and wooden rails – all of which had to be jumped cleanly if no faults were to be awarded by the judges.
>
> Indoor competitions were run in Paris around 1880. The Royal Dublin Society moved its Horse Show from the lawn of Leinster House to its new premises at Ballsbridge in 1881. The New York Horse Show was begun at Madison Square Garden in 1883. Jumping was included in the Paris Olympics of 1900 and became a full Olympic sport in 1912 at Stockholm.
>
> When the first Balmoral Show took place in 1896, it included this "new sport" in its programme and created its own magnificent arena to accommodate it. This oval was one of the best in the world and with constant upgrading over the years it remains so.
>
> In the early days, and through the first quarter of this century, the course at Balmoral very much resembled those used at the Olympic Games or in the growing number of Nations Cup meetings at places like London, San Sebastian, Brussels, Turin, Rome and The Hague. But there was one essential difference that was unique to Ireland from the beginning – the double bank, single bank and stone wall were included.
>
> Efforts to further develop the sport were curtailed by the First World War, but after that conflict, great strides were made internationally in the creation of Nations Cup meetings and the establishment of military teams. In 1921 the

International Equestrian Federation was formed, and in 1926 the First Nations Cup meeting was held at the RDS, Ballsbridge. Some six years later, Ireland became affiliated to the Fédération Equestre Internationale (FEI).

During these years between the wars, the Annual Show at Balmoral became a nursery for Show Jumping, taking place each May after the Spring Show in Dublin and in the run-up to important events all around the island, including the Dublin Horse Show.

Riders like Jim Bryson, Jack Bamber, Billy McCully, and the Honourable John Brooke were enthused by these competitions at Balmoral and got the desire for the sport which was to stay with them all their lives. They and many others became powerful forces in the development and formation of Show Jumping in Ireland both before and after the Second World War.

Until the Second World War, the Nations Cup teams were all military riders and they remained so for a time after the War. But during the Fifties and early Sixties what was to be called a "Civilian Team" began to take form. People like Maurice Bamber, Jim Bryson, Brian McNicoll and Barney McGlone of Limavady, John Brooke, Billy McCully and others joined with people like Tommy Brennan, Leslie Fitzpatrick, Iris Kellett, Seamus Hayes and Tommy Wade on these teams. During the Sixties, competition among these riders at places like Balmoral was keen and an interprovincial team event run like the Aga Khan Trophy was held during these years. Lady riders including Iris Kellett, Mrs Garland, Mrs Joan Morrison, Mrs St John Nolan and Diana Connolly Carew took part.

Miss Iris Kellett played a leading part in the formation in 1945 of the Horse Jumping and Riding Encouragement Association of Ireland. Here she competes at Balmoral in 1947 on 'Rusty'.

Billy McCully was introduced to show horses at an early age by his father Hugh, himself a leading horseman. Obviously protective headgear, with chin strap fitted, was not in the Rule Book at that time.

Billy McCully, a legendary rider whose exploits and anecdotes are worth a separate chapter or indeed a book recalls:

> A number of the Northern owners formed the Northern Ireland Show Jumping Association in 1945, and the first event under Show Jumping Association rules was held at Donacloney. Some of the main people involved were Captain Hugh Morrison of Aghadowey, David McCreedy of Banbridge, Herbie Forbes of Belfast, 'Packie' McEntee of Clones, Jim Bryson of Loughbrickland, Jack Bamber of Ballymena, Willie Allen of Moira, Jack Heather of Banbridge, Dick Collon of Portadown and Dublin, Dick Garland of Newry and Johnny Reid of Banbridge. The first Secretary of the Association was Alfie Quinn from Banbridge. In the same year Colonel Dudgeon, and Iris Kellett from the South formed the Horse Jumping and Riding Encouragement Association of Ireland but 'certain matters were retained to the discretion of the separate areas'. Then in 1954, these two bodies joined together to become the Show Jumping Association of Ireland, and the amalgamation meeting was held at Ballymascanlon Hotel near Dundalk on 14 April. There was no such thing as instant agreement and over the next period there were constant and passionate discussions about what flag and anthem the Irish team would use. But gradually good sense prevailed and these potentially contentious matters were considered, and in the long run agreement was reached.

The Irish Show Jumping Team which travelled to Glasgow in 1949 line up with their trophy – but no sign of the improvised 'Irish' flag!

Early on, however, there was a story which put all the talk about flags in perspective. I was a very young member of an Irish team which went to compete in Glasgow. I took the Downpatrick flag with me but on the way across on the boat we fell in with a crowd of theatrical people travelling from Belfast, and quite a few refreshments were taken. The upshot was that I lost the flag, so we had nothing to carry in the parade in Glasgow. So we went to a billiard hall and asked for a length of green baize. We made that into a green 'flag' to carry in front of the Irish team during the parade and nobody in the crowd was any the wiser!

Billy McCully rode a number of times for Ireland but those were the years when military riders were dominant on Irish teams, and civilians had much less opportunity of showing their ability. Billy, however, won almost innumerable trophies and championships, and in 1956 he made national headlines when he had a nasty fall at Harringay Arena in the presence of the Queen and Prince Philip, and in full view of the television cameras. The *Daily Mail* reported:

> More than 100 people collapsed and were carried sick and fainting from their seats at the Horse of the Year Show at Harringay Arena last night after a rider crashed in front of the Queen and the Duke of Edinburgh.

Whilst Billy McCully made national headlines in 1956, following his fall from November's Eve at Harringay in front of the Queen and Prince Philip, he had previously scaled the heights with this horse, as witnessed by his victory in the Balmoral Championship in May 1953. November's Eve is seen jumping a brush fence during the competition.

> Officials turned the Press room into a casualty clearing station. One woman said: "When we saw the rider twitching on the ground, we thought he had broken his neck and was dying."
>
> Millions of television viewers saw the rider, William McCully of County Down, carried to the first-aid room on a stretcher. Doctors said he had concussion. He came round and briefly recognised his wife. Then he was taken, unconscious again, to hospital.

However, there was a happy ending – the *Daily Telegraph* reported later in the week:

> Mr W McCully, who has been under doctor's orders since his bad fall on Wednesday night, gained a brilliant victory at the Horse of the Year Show tonight in the Daily Telegraph Cup. He was riding the same horse November's Eve, and it was an Irish success, the first of the week.

Despite being dislodged by November's Eve in front of the Queen, a large crowd and millions of television viewers, Willie McCully looks back on the horse as one of the best he ever rode.

> She was not always great at the smaller shows but she always rose to the big occasion. I was also very fond of Ballyblack. He and I got on very well and he took me out of trouble on many occasions. "Happy" was a brilliant horse, and he would be worth half-a-million today. He could do anything. Whether it was Greyabbey gymkhana or the Horse of the Year Show his main ambition was to get round without knocking anything down. He was a real winner!

Billy McCully has spent a lifetime with horses. He developed a love for Show Jumping through his father Hugh who was also a very well-known and a successful rider. Despite all Billy McCully's great successes, his motto remains simple "A good horse makes a good horseman". It is a modest motto for a rider who was so consistent and distinguished in the decades after World War Two.

In July 1971, a most successful International competition was held at Balmoral, in conjunction with the Show Jumping Association of Ireland, and sponsored by the steel firm Gambles Simms. It received widespread pre-publicity and with the prospect of household names like David Broome and Harvey Smith taking part, the event was assured of a large attendance. David Broome, as expected, showed why he was the current world champion when he won both the International events on the first day. He rode Ballywillwill to victory in the Gambles Simms Ulster 71 Stakes, and later took the Irene Dawson Stakes on Manhatten by 0.6 of a second ahead of Dubliner Tommy Brennan. Miss Anne Lowry, who was a leading figure in the Show Jumping world, kept the local flag flying by finishing third in the Gambles Simms Ulster 71 Stakes behind David Broome and Harvey Smith. Lord Lowry, her father, looks back on that most successful event:

> The competitors included not only David Broome and Harvey Smith but also the entire Danish Team (chef d'équipe Knud Larsen) for the Dublin Horse Show, as well as its leading Irish riders. Granville Nugent, who did so much for good relations in the equestrian world, was asked by the Northern Region to act as President of the Ground Jury and Joap Rijks of Holland (later Treasurer of the FEI) was the Foreign Judge. There were six International jumping competitions, and a wide variety of National horse and pony competitions and showing classes.
>
> The success of the Show, held in beautiful weather, owed much to the inspired work of Mrs Pamela Carruthers the famous International course designer from Hickstead, who quickly got the measure of her field and produced some wonderful jumping. The Governor of Northern Ireland, Lord Grey of Naunton, honoured the Show by his presence on the third day and took the salute in the Grand Prix. All the visitors were full of praise for the jumping arena and its beautiful setting and for the welcome which they received. David Broome and Harvey Smith, in particular, were great ambassadors for their

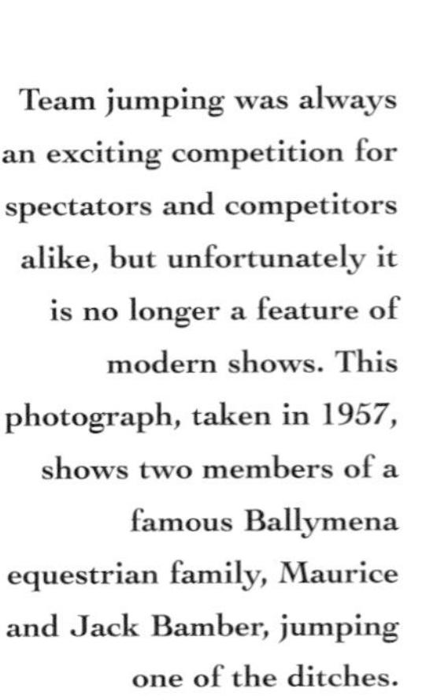

Team jumping was always an exciting competition for spectators and competitors alike, but unfortunately it is no longer a feature of modern shows. This photograph, taken in 1957, shows two members of a famous Ballymena equestrian family, Maurice and Jack Bamber, jumping one of the ditches.

> country. Not only did they enjoy a successful Show, but they spent hours signing autographs and took a most enthusiastic interest in the young riders' and pony competitions.

The event was not repeated, however, mainly due to the Troubles and it was some 17 years later that top-class International Show Jumping returned to Balmoral. This was intimated in the Minutes of the Show Jumping Sub-Committee of the Society which met on 30 September 1987, under the Chairmanship of Sam Martin.

> Although, in recent years, the standard of jumping had improved, in an effort to make further improvements and to create more spectator interest it had been suggested that the Show Jumping section of the Balmoral Show should attain International status. Initially, this would involve inviting four/five top riders from Great Britain (amongst those suggested were the Whittaker Brothers, Malcolm Pyrah, Harvey Smith) and Lord Lowry agreed to study the implications of this within the structure of the FEI Rules. Mr John Dawson submitted a proposed programme to incorporate International competitions together with a number of National competitions.
>
> To be attractive a considerable increase in prize money would be necessary,

requiring more sponsorship. Initial enquiries to possible sponsors had been encouraging and would be helped further if the BBC's plans to televise the Show on Network . . . came to fruition.

The matter was taken up again at the next meeting of the Show Jumping Sub-Committee, on 21 October 1987.

The Lord Lowry, having studied the implications of the holding of an International Show Jumping Event at Balmoral, recommended that such be run under FEI General Regulation 106 as a CF (Frontier event) where International competitions are open to individual competitors from the home Nation and one foreign Nation and must be held under FEI Jumping Rules. This would restrict "foreign" riders to those from Great Britain and would not, for example, allow an Australian, domiciled in Great Britain, to appear unless he had elected to ride as a GB competitor for the season concerned.

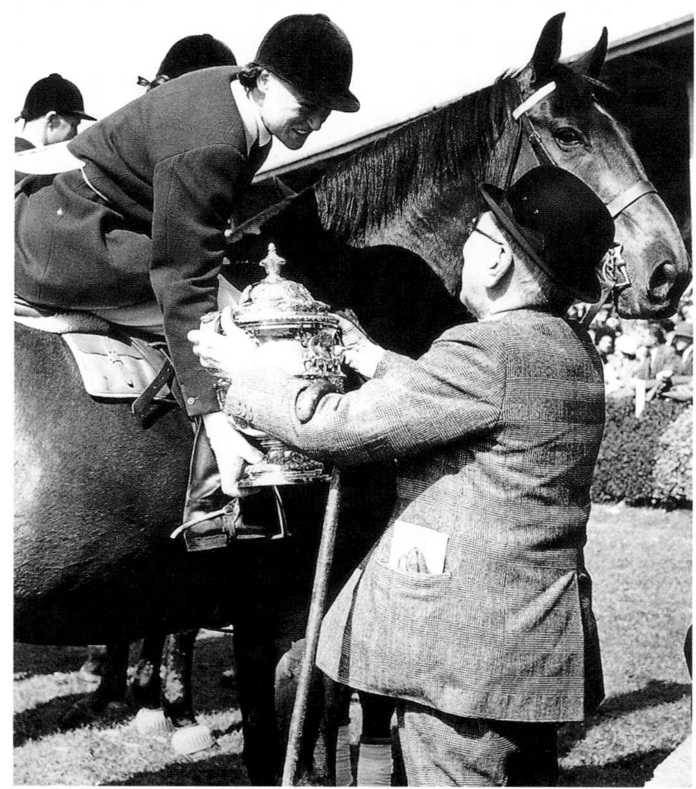

Chester Nugent was very deeply involved in the equestrian activities of the Society and presented the Chester Nugent Gold Cup to be competed for annually in the major Show Jumping competition (The Show Championship). He is seen here handing the trophy to the 1961 winner Mrs Morrison. This impressive cup is on display throughout the year in the Trophy Cabinet in the foyer of the Balmoral Conference Centre.

It was agreed that the Chief Executive should write to Miss Michelle Knapp, Secretary General of the Equestrian Federation of Ireland seeking approval, in principle, of the holding of a CF Event at Balmoral. A copy of this letter to be forwarded to Ned Campion of the SJAI, for information, and the Chief Executive also to speak informally with Commander Bill Jeffries with regard to seeking approval from the British Federation.

Mr Dawson indicated that all the riders contacted by him had expressed interest in coming to Balmoral although it was too early to obtain confirmation until the 1988 calendar of International Team events was finalised . . . It was agreed that riders invited to Balmoral from Great Britain would be provided with a free ferry crossing, together with hotel accommodation whilst in Belfast. Appearance money would not be provided as it was hoped that the Prize Fund would be attractive enough. (Another important factor was the up-grading of the Arena in the Seventies, under the direction of the course-builder Steve Hickey.)

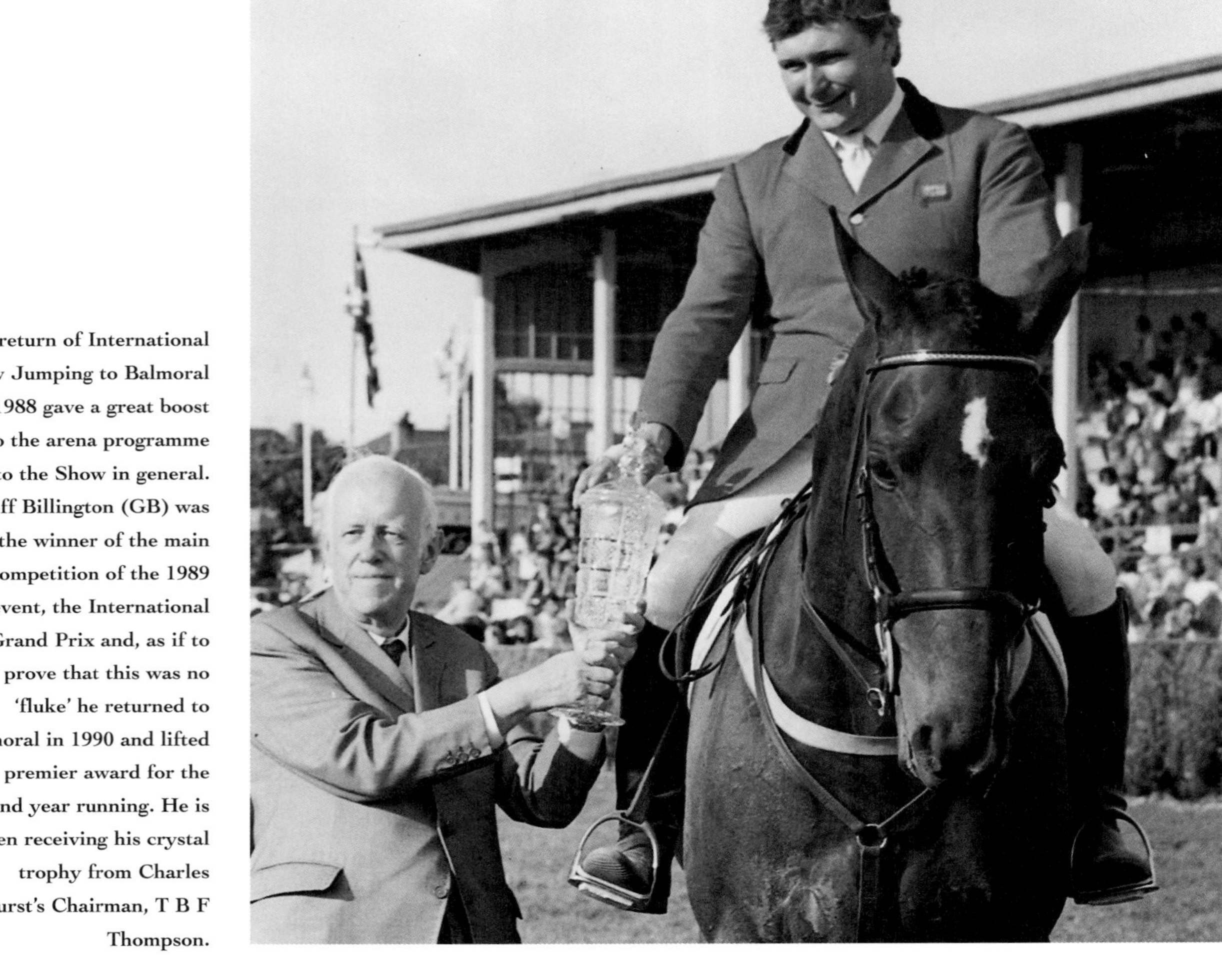

The return of International Show Jumping to Balmoral in 1988 gave a great boost to the arena programme and to the Show in general. Geoff Billington (GB) was the winner of the main competition of the 1989 event, the International Grand Prix and, as if to prove that this was no 'fluke' he returned to Balmoral in 1990 and lifted the premier award for the second year running. He is seen receiving his crystal trophy from Charles Hurst's Chairman, T B F Thompson.

The Sub-Committee's work bore fruit, and the magazine *Horse and Hound* of 5 May 1988 reported that two major sponsors – Carlsberg and Ballygowan Spring Water - had agreed to back an International event which, the magazine reported "is seen as a major breakthrough for the sport in Northern Ireland".

The good news was announced by the Society in a Press Release which stated:

> Top class International Show Jumping will return to Northern Ireland for the first time in over a decade at this year's Balmoral Show. The cream of British and Irish show jumpers will be there competing for a total prize fund of £17,500. Included in the line-up will be many household names including Harvey and Robert Smith, Michael Whitaker, Paul Darragh, Jack Doyle, Trevor Coyle and Vina Lyons. Highlight of the Show will be the Ballygowan

> Spring Water Grand Prix with a prize fund of £6,000. This prestigious event will commence on Thursday, 19 May at 4.00 pm. Adding a further competitive edge to the event will be the desire of many of the riders to compete in this year's Olympics. Taking place in the morning will be the Carlsberg Parcours de Chasse, a competition designed to demonstrate horses' obedience, hardiness and speed. There is also a full programme of International Show Jumping arranged for the first two days of the Show including on Tuesday competitions sponsored by Dalgety Spillers and Mitsubishi, while on Wednesday two further events are sponsored by Next and Belfast Ferries.
>
> Mr Bill Yarr, Chief Executive of the RUAS, said: "A lot of hard work has gone into preparing for these prestigious events. I am glad to say that our efforts have borne fruit, and that visitors to the Show can be guaranteed a display of high class Show Jumping. The RUAS was extremely keen to facilitate the staging of these competitions, and we hope that the foundations laid this year can be built upon in the future."

The 12 May edition of *Horse and Hound* underlined the wider importance. It stated: "Balmoral is of particular interest on the Irish horse scene, since it provides the first outing of the season for both the young horses and the four-year-old hunters. In many cases, the winners here go on to be the main challengers in Dublin."

The event proved to be highly successful and the Show Stewards Committee noted that the "International Show Jumping Events had provided top-class jumping with maximum media coverage, and highly complimentary remarks made by visiting riders and officials." It was strongly recommended that International Show Jumping should become a regular feature of the Balmoral Shows.

Harvey Smith, a competitor in the 1988 International event, was fulsome in his praise. Writing in the 26 May edition of *Horse and Hound* he stated:

> The Friendly Balmoral International Show in Northern Ireland last week attracted big crowds and in spite of the explosion, it created the good old-fashioned atmosphere of a real traditional agricultural show.
>
> I haven't competed there since 1971, so I found quite a few things had changed. The main Arena used to be bigger than Royal Dublin, but this time it was about half the size. But the whole thing has developed along the right lines and the people who run Dublin could learn a lot from Balmoral.
>
> Balmoral is the perfect lesson in how to mix an agricultural show with good show jumping. Horses were part of the Show and this was the first time it had staged International jumping since that year, 1971.

In recent years there have been a number of Northern Ireland riders who have met with considerable success not only on home ground but also on the world scene. Trevor Coyle of Portadown is one of these and he had a particularly spectacular season in 1995. He is a great supporter of Balmoral (and a past winner of the International Grand Prix in 1992). He is seen winning the Harberton Competition at the 1995 Show on his ten year old grey stallion Cruising, prior to winning many other competitions across Europe – as well as a major success at the Spruce Meadows masters event in Calgary. The highlight of his season, however, was his role in Ireland's Nations Cup team which won the coveted Aga Khan Trophy at the Dublin Horse Show.

He added a philosophic comment about his own show jumping fortunes.

> My horses are all suffering from "four-faultitis" at the moment. But I'm not worried, they are not kicking out three or four fences, just one. So it's all about patience and time; the clear rounds will arrive.

The recommendation that Balmoral should continue to stage International events was taken up by the Society, and in recent years there has been an impressive display of prize-winners. In 1990 Geoff Billington on Rhapsody won the Charles Hurst Grand Prix for the second year in a row, and a year later Jessica Chesney from Cullybackey won on Diamond Exchange. In 1992 Trevor Coyle, with Golda, won the top prize for the third time, and in 1993 Edward Doyle, a new Irish team member, won with Multiform. He went on to become Irish Champion in 1995. In 1994 Martin Lucas won the NIE Grand Prix for Britain with Senator Acrobat and in 1995 the winner was Robert Splaine with his King George V Gold Cup winner Heather Blaze. Sadly, this plucky mare fell at the water-jump at the 1995 Dublin Horse Show, and had to be put down.

It is also worth noting that the constant up-grading of Balmoral in the Seventies and Eighties greatly helped the local riders. Michael Slavin notes:

> During a 20 year period every rider from the Northern Region who made it on to the Irish International team did well at Balmoral – the list includes James Kernan, Trevor Coyle, Jessica Chesney, Margaret Creighton, Vina Buller, Linda Courtney, Stephen Smith, Harry Marshall and a number of others.

Show Jumping at Balmoral, like Balmoral and the RUAS, has come a long way in the past 100 years. The bigger prize money and increasing competition has pushed up standards, while the advent of television and wider media coverage has increased the popularity of the sport. The wordy reporter whose eye-witness accounts of the first Show at Balmoral in 1896 would be astounded at the progress if he were alive today, but he would have the satisfaction of a prophecy fulfilled - 100 years ago he forecast that the Balmoral "jumping ground will be a really splendid one". How right he was!

Milk quotas were unheard of at the time when this was the standard method of milking. (Photograph from the W A Green Collection, Ulster Museum.)

A CENTURY OF PROGRESS *Chapter 9*

IN THE PAST CENTURY SINCE THE FIRST AGRICULTURAL SHOW took place at Balmoral, farming has made remarkable progress. One man who is well-placed to look at these changes in perspective and to cast an eye on the future is Dr James Young, former Principal of Loughry College, Cookstown, former Permanent Secretary at the Department of Agriculture from 1966-83 and a Vice President of the RUAS since 1984. "Jimmy" Young, who is well-known to the agricultural community in Northern Ireland and further afield, gives his considered views on farming – past, present and future.

Dr James Young, Permanent Secretary, Department of Agriculture for Northern Ireland 1966 – 1983 and a Vice President of the Society.

> It has changed from being almost a way of life for about 225,000 people (including farmers' wives and farm employees) to being a scientific business for some 60,000 people. There has been a steady movement from the land to new jobs in manufacturing and service industries. The net result has been fewer and larger farms with greater scope for and emphasis on management and specialisation.
>
> During the same period the total volume of gross output of crops, livestock and livestock products has increased 3.5 times, so the output per person has gone up about 13 fold.

The modern technique of harvesting is a far cry from this method of cutting and binding grass with an "automatic machine". (Photograph from the W A Green Collection, Ulster Museum.)

As well there is now much more emphasis on quality of produce and efficient marketing – a development aided by the Northern Ireland agricultural marketing legislation of the 1930's. Among other things this legislation laid down quality standards and provided for the setting up of the Agricultural Marketing Boards for pigs and milk, followed later by seed potatoes. Subsequent legislation provided for the Livestock Marketing Commission, which is still functioning.

While the Marketing Boards have now given way to other bodies they made a valuable contribution to marketing and processing from the 1930's onwards. All this together with the improvement of communication between food retailers, processors and producers has led to a vast expansion of food processing in Northern Ireland. Today practically all the farm produce grown on Northern Ireland farms is processed in Northern Ireland. Gone are the days, for instance, when it was common to see large droves of cattle being taken to the docks in Belfast for shipment to England or Scotland.

As farming became more lucrative the use of balanced fertilisers, compound feeding stuffs, pesticides and herbicides increased. The supply of these together with food processing now provides employment for about 24,000 people, or roughly 3 times the number 100 years ago. All this progress has been encouraged in a variety of ways.

In the first place education, research and development work in agriculture and food processing at Queen's University, the Agricultural Research Institute, Hillsborough, and the three colleges at Greenmount, Enniskillen and Loughry

Fair Day at Castlewellan, as this heavily pregnant sow awaits a new home. (Photograph from the W A Green Collection, Ulster Museum.)

together with the farm and horticulture advisory services have provided much of the know-how for efficiency and expansion, while the guaranteed prices for farm products introduced during the Second World War (and continued thereafter) have provided the incentive. Strict animal health controls and disease eradication schemes have made expansion of livestock numbers more feasible.

Another important factor was that during the last 100 years practically every Northern Ireland farmer became the owner of his farm. This was made possible by a series of UK Acts of Parliament between 1870 and 1925 which enabled all tenants to purchase their farms from their landlords. The Government paid the landlords and the farmers recouped the cost to the government through payment of annuities for a period of years. This gave Northern Ireland farmers the confidence to invest money improving and developing their farms.

The formation of the Ulster Farmers' Union in 1918 and the Young Farmers' Clubs of Ulster in 1929 were also important milestones in Northern Ireland agriculture. Both have made a valuable contribution to the development of the industry. The Ulster Farmers' Union has played a most useful role in representing the interests of farmers to Government and other relevant bodies. This has been of particular importance since the introduction of guaranteed prices and other support measures. The Young Farmers' Club movement with

Prior to the building of the Central Exhibition Hall, the then Ministry of Agriculture presented their Balmoral Show display in the Londonderry Hall. This exhibition, promoting the vigour and fecundity of Egg Production, was presented in 1924 and may well have been the first such Ministry display at Balmoral following the partition of Ireland.

its motto "Better Farmers: Better Countrymen: Better Citizens" and its extensive programme of competitions has added greatly to the social and educational development of young country people (both male and female) and has done much to link town and country.

Other specialist bodies representing various sectors of the Northern Ireland agricultural and food industries have also made valuable contributions.

The development of radio broadcasting following the formation of the British Broadcasting Company in 1922 (and its transformation to the British Broadcasting Corporation on 1 January 1927) and of Television in later years altered the pattern of life, especially in rural areas. The BBC not only removed the isolation of rural dwellers but also for many years produced regular specialist programmes for farmers and horticulturalists. These brought valuable advice and information into the farmhouse.

The coming of the motor car and motorised transport gave farmers and their families mobility. This provided easy access to town and even city facilities and was a further factor in breaking down the barrier between town and country. This barrier practically disappeared during the past 50 to 70 years with the connection of practically all farms and farmhouses to mains electricity and water supplies and to telephone services.

The Ministry moved the location of their display to the Central Exhibition Hall (now called the Balmoral Hall) when it was built in 1926. At other times of the year the Hall was used for a variety of purposes. Lines from badminton courts slightly overpower the Ministry's display at the 1937 Show, although by the look of the stains on the floor, they probably had a more serious problem to deal with – a badly leaking roof!

Some 50 years ago the introduction of the artificial insemination service by the then Ministry of Agriculture was a very important factor in the improvement of cattle. This made available to every Northern Ireland farmer semen from the best bulls worldwide. The improvement of other farm animals has been encouraged by a variety of official recording and testing schemes.

During the past 20 years UK membership of the EC has made an impact on farming through changes in the price support system and the resultant surpluses of farm products, leading to new developments such as quotas and set-aside. It is too early to pronounce judgement on the longer term effects of EC membership.

Concern for the environment has been an increasingly important factor in agricultural policy and practice over the past 20 to 30 years and clearly will continue to be an important consideration in future.

Accompanying all this progress has been a variety of physical changes affecting farming – all obvious even to the casual observer. For example, the traditional country fairs have practically disappeared together with the old practice of hiring farm workers on a yearly or half-yearly basis. Farm animals are now sold either at auction marts or direct to bacon factories or meat plants.

Most farmhouses have been modernised with the benefit of grant aid, electricity and running water. The farm family is now much less reliant on home-grown foods and consumes a share of the wide variety of frozen and other processed foods available in shops and supermarkets. Sophisticated food processing plants and food retailers now exist throughout Northern Ireland, covering (among other things) fruit and vegetables, eggs, milk, meat of all kinds and fish.

During the past 60 years practically all farm horses and horse-drawn equipment have been replaced by tractors and associated equipment – a development which owes much to the genius of the late Harry Ferguson He developed the hydraulic lift which made tractors and tractor-operated machinery a realistic option for Northern Ireland farmers from the mid-1930's onwards. The total number of tractors in Northern Ireland is now over 40,000. The number of farm horses is now negligible compared with 125,000 in 1895 although there is a growing interest in riding horses and ponies which together now number about 10,000.

The contribution made by Harry Ferguson to the development of mechanisation of farm machinery is legendary. He is seen here at the 1948 Balmoral Show touring the machinery exhibits with (right) Lord Glentoran and (left) Secretary/Manager Sam Clarke.

The humble scythe which was a common tool on most farms (especially the smaller farms) up to about 1940 is now largely a museum piece.

The increase in the volume of gross output mentioned earlier did not indicate the large changes which have taken place in the make-up of that output. There has been a reduction in tillage crops (notably oats and potatoes), greatly improved grassland with a switch from hay to grass silage for winter fodder and large increases in the numbers of livestock. The most relevant figures for areas of crops and numbers of livestock at 1 June 1895 and 1994 are given in the following table.

Areas of Crops (Thousand Hectares)			**Numbers of Livestock** (Thousand Head)		
	1895	**1994**		**1895**	**1994**
Wheat	4.5	7.0	Cows for Milk		274
Barley	0.9	33.4		303	
Oats	163.0	2.4	Cows for Beef		279
Flax	29.0	Negligible	All Cattle	783	1,581
Potatoes	80.0	8.4	All Sheep	351	2,531
Hay	170.0	29.2	All Pigs	245	562
Grass for Silage	Negligible	268.1	All Poultry	2,800	13,643

In 1994, as a means of recognising the centenary of the incorporation of the Society under the Educational Endowments Act, a number of plaques were presented to trade exhibitors who had supported the Royal Ulster by taking trade space at successive Balmoral Shows for fifty or more years. One of these was Sam McCormick who first exhibited in 1936. Over the years his company's stands have displayed the most up-to-date farm machinery available. This stand, at the 1958 Show, despite the obvious wet weather, attracted much attention with its display of International tractors and implements.

Other important changes in crops and livestock during the past 100 years include:

Mushroom production developed from scratch to about 20 million lb in 1994. The greater part of this development has taken place during the past 30 years. About 85% of this production is sold outside Northern Ireland mostly in England.

The efficiency of vegetable production has been greatly increased by the use of F1 hybrid seed which gives higher yields and more uniformity and by the use of herbicides to control weeds.

The area of flax reached a high of close to 50,000 hectares during the Second World War but fell to a very small experimental area because, being no longer of national importance, price support was discontinued a few years after the war ended.

During the past 25 years various Continental breeds of beef cattle have been imported mainly because they have a higher growth rate and produce leaner beef than UK domestic breeds. The latter have lost ground, particularly the Shorthorn.

Although the total number of pigs in 1994 is just over double that in 1895 it is only about half of the peak figure reached in 1971. The fall since 1971 has resulted mainly from the loss of access to relatively cheap supplies of grain on the world market following UK entry to the EEC in 1973.

- The broiler industry has developed since the end of the war and now broilers make up more than half of the total number of poultry. Broilers have always been kept intensively indoors. That has also applied to laying hens since the early 1950's when the deep litter system replaced free range. Later most egg producers switched to battery cages although in recent years a few have allowed their birds to range to meet a limited demand for free range eggs. Both broiler and egg production have for several years been controlled mainly by the processors and packers through contracts with producers.
- The travelling threshing machines and the gathering together of neighbours to thresh the oats, wheat and barley during the winter months used to be a feature of the countryside but have disappeared completely.
- Stackyards with their neatly trimmed stacks of oats etc have suffered a similar fate, as combine harvesters have taken over the harvesting of grain. Another casualty on many farms has been the midden – replaced by the slurry tank.

In view of all the features that have disappeared it is comforting to note that, despite the progress and the drift from the land, the family farm is still predominant.

It is also comforting to note that during the past 100 years the Royal Ulster Agricultural Society has grown from strength to strength and is fully geared to serve the present day and future agriculture and food industries. The RUAS has provided and still provides a very valuable focus and unifying force for farmers, breeders of riding horses, suppliers of farm machinery, fertilisers etc and food processors and retailers. The Society has developed beyond recognition and retains the very important role of providing a shop window for all these industries to display the steadily improving quality of their products and of farm livestock at its Shows and Sales.

The future of Northern Ireland agriculture is bound to be affected by the way in which the Common Agriculture Policy (CAP) of the EC develops. The high cost of the CAP is already causing concern and as the EC is further enlarged (bringing in new countries with very different agricultural industries) it is likely that substantial changes will have to be made to the CAP.

At best this will create uncertainty, particularly in view of the surpluses of most commodities which already exist and which are already creating pressure for lower prices and making it more difficult to improve efficiency by increasing production.

As hi-tech methods in other industries and services are making full employment more remote it will be more difficult in future for efficiency in farming to be increased by shedding labour to these other industries and services as happened in the past. At the same time farmers will be under increasing pressure to protect the environment and to pay even more attention to consumer demand.

In the light of these pressures farmers are almost certain to make further changes to keep their standard of living in line with that of other people.

The Ministry and (from 1973) the Department of Agriculture for Northern Ireland has always recognised the importance to the industry of staging a comprehensive educational exhibit at Balmoral Show. Much thought and effort is put into the presentation of displays, and although the exhibition has not been eligible for the best Trade Stand Award at the Show, the Judge in 1989 felt that the DANI presentation deserved some reward. This specially engraved pewter plate was subsequently presented to the Department, and has proudly been displayed since then outside the Permanent Secretary's office in Dundonald House.

Firstly, there will probably be increasing emphasis on quality of product through quality assurance schemes and, in some cases, through extension of the contract farming in the poultry industry to other commodities eg pigs and some horticultural products.

Secondly, the trend to greater specialisation is likely to continue under the influence of still more economic pressure.

Thirdly, the need to find new or alternative enterprises on some farms is likely to increase. Such enterprises could arise from new demands as the standard of living rises. For example, the steadily growing demand for bedding plants and horticultural nursery stock should provide opportunities for some local growers. Again there may be scope for the breeding and rearing of more riding horses and ponies, cashing in on Northern Ireland's growing reputation in this field – a reputation enhanced steadily by the Royal Ulster Agricultural Society. Here may also be scope for the extension of some existing fringe activities such as open farms, ostrich and deer farming and private afforestation of some land.

If terrorism ends for good, tourism will increase and this would provide an opportunity for more farmers and their wives to open guest houses and possibly start other enterprises such as pony trekking. It is unlikely that any of these approaches could match existing enterprises but together they might ease the pressure on those enterprises if even a few farmers adopt them.

Despite the introduction of many continental sheep breeds over the years, there is still a major following for the traditional Blackface upland breed. This shearling ram, owned by Roger Crawford of Parkmore, Ballymena was the 1981 Blackface Champion, much to the delight of Roger's son Gordon. (Photograph: Wilfred Green)

Finally, whatever approaches individual farmers take in future, the greatest single need for all will be to maintain the highest possible level of efficiency. This can only be done by keeping management accounts and the use of the best available strains of livestock and varieties of crops combined with the latest information to keep overhead costs low and to maximise gross margins.

(Note: The statistics used in this Chapter have been kindly supplied by the Economics & Statistics Division of the Northern Ireland Department of Agriculture.)

Short trousers and waistcoat was the preferred dress for this young gentleman as he brushes the coat of an impressive Aberdeen Angus bull at the 1936 Annual Show. It is not clear if those behind the animal are struck by its considerable presence or are merely waiting in the queue for 'the Gents'.

MEMORIES AND MILESTONES *Chapter 10*

THE HISTORY OF THE ROYAL ULSTER AGRICULTURAL SOCIETY and its antecedents, and of the Balmoral Show itself, is not told by statistics alone, nor by events, nor the work of committees, nor marked only by the visits of Royalty and of other distinguished guests. Its' history is the sum of the lives and experiences of countless people whose contributions and participation made the Society what it is today. Many of the older people whose memories stretched to the turn of the century, and beyond, have passed on but their reminiscences have been recorded for posterity. Others in the twilight of their lives still retain clear recollections, while others still are young and vibrant enough to notice and to comment on more recent changes and developments. They all add up to a colourful and changing mosaic of one of the lasting institutions of Ulster life.

Norman Scott, always a picture of sartorial elegance and never without a buttonhole.

One of the earliest recollections was that of the late Norman Scott, a well-known character of sartorial elegance who had an abiding interest in the horticultural section of the Show. His first visit to Balmoral was around 1906 when, as a pupil at Malone National School, he got into the Show by squeezing through a thorn-hedge. He not so much 'gate-crashed' as hedge-crashed'! One of the features of the early Shows was the transport. He recalled:

> There were several platforms on the railway lines opposite Malone Presbyterian Church and it was like an agricultural station. There were a great

many visitors from the Irish Republic in those days, and there were special trains that stopped at Balmoral, where the people left to go to the Show and where the livestock were de-boxed. Although there were very few ladies in the early days, the Dublin people used to arrive with their wives, and that brought the others in.

One of the great features was the Show horses.

There were the carriers like Warleys and Thomas Johnstons with their Clydesdales and their brasses beautifully polished, and with different decorations. I remember a two-horse bread-cart, which was a tremendous attraction.

All kinds of people came from all parts of Ulster, and beyond, for the Show.

My mother had a cousin who lived near Ballycastle, and when the Show dates were settled we used to get a postcard taken out of a very old album. It was addressed to my mother and it said ' Me and another boy will be up for the Show, signed Tommy'. They brought two parcels wrapped in newspapers, which were set on the hall table. Nobody asked what they were until our visitors left. Then my mother opened the parcels which contained a boiling fowl and a bunch of rhubarb. That was to pay for their keep. They were great characters.

Lucy McKinstry (nee Ward) was an active member of the Young Farmers' Clubs of Ulster and her talents, along with those of John Gibson, were rewarded in a YFCU Debating Competition held just prior to the Second World War.

The late Mrs Lucy McKinstry, recalled in her early Eighties, going to Shows long before The King's Hall was built.

I remember the Twenties when the Show had a most beautiful layout of flowers and shrubs. One of my earliest memories was that of a horse with a kind of watering device which sprayed the flowers early in the morning when people arrived for the Show." Her father, a Mr John Ward, was a member of the RUAS and she recalls: "The family went by bus from Hillsborough and it was a great day out. There were nine in our family, two boys and seven girls, so we could not all go in the one day. Somebody had to stay behind and look after the work.

I remember my father telling me about his parents going to the Show in the latter years of the last century by pony and trap. They came from near Dromore and stabled the pony somewhere at Finaghy Road South. They then walked to Balmoral, stayed all day and walked back to the stables. Then they rode home in the trap and slept all the way back. The pony brought them alone! My own visits as a child to Balmoral were very special. That was one of the big days out in the year. There was nothing else, except maybe a Sunday School excursion to the seaside.

Lucy remembered going dancing in later years, as a young girl.

They held Young Farmers dances in the Orpheus Ballroom in Belfast, and there might be up to 1,000 people in the hall. It was always a great night, but of course we would be tired the next day. My father was a bit strict and did not approve of dancing, so we passed it off in some other way. We did not want to tell him lies.

I went to College at Loughry and Strabane but came back home to the farm when one of my sisters died. We did the milking by hand, because there were no such things as milk parlours. Some of my happiest days on the farm were out in the fields, lifting the potatoes by hand and tying corn and hay. There were many stories about the early farming days. Someone told me about a farm near Seymour Hill where they used to put a couple of hundred geese on the corn fields to fatten them up. They would be driven along the main road by a couple of young boys. I would love to have seen them walking down the road – it must have been a wonderful sight.

There are great memories, too, about some of the early sheep and cow 'drives'. There was a farmer who brought over sheep from Scotland and he 'walked' them by stages from Belfast to Donacloney. The sheep were being driven along Cromac Street in Belfast when a ram saw his reflection in the window of a bakery and charged right through the plate glass! That night the sheep and the sheepdog rested in a yard at Lambeg and set off the next morning for Donacloney. The dog did the 'driving' and the farmer went by pony and trap. I also remember people talking about driving cattle from Hilltown to Dundrum and then putting them on a boat for Scotland. They had made shoes for the cattle to help protect them on their journey.

In my youth I developed skills in public speaking and in stock-judging, as part of the Young Farmers' Clubs. Later I also developed an eye for a bargain! I've been to auctions all over Ireland and there was hardly a big house I wasn't in. I would buy pieces of silver and good furniture with the money I made from the hens. Traditionally the farmer's wife got the hen money!

I went to the Balmoral Show for many years until failing health prevented me from doing so. My lasting impression of the Show in later years was its size. It was vast compared to the earlier days and it was much easier to get to. Instead of going by bus and partly on foot I could simply park my car at my sister's house near Balmoral. That was a great improvement, and so too were the developments in machinery. That made a big difference to farmers and their families and to life on the farm.

Frank Dickson has always been a great supporter of the Society and despite being in his mid 80's, he is still an active steward at Pig Shows and Sales and in the Cattle Section at the Annual Show. (Photograph: Alf McCreary)

Frank Dickson, a Council member for many years and a Vice President of the Society has the remarkable record of attending some 75 Balmoral Shows. In his 86th year he recalled clearly his experiences.

My earliest memory of the Show was going with my father on a motorbike and side-car around 1917. There were just sheds, consisting of galvanised iron or wood covered with felt, and inside the gate where The King's Hall is situated now, they held the main machinery display. The cattle, as I remember, were all housed in wooden sheds with felt roofs. In those days there were two separate sections, and you paid an admission fee to the Show which did not include the jumping enclosure. So those who were interested in horses and jumping did not circulate much in the main Show. I suppose about 60% of the cattle were Shorthorn, with the next biggest section Aberdeen Angus, and it was a struggle early on to get classes for Herefords and British Friesians. Our family was very keen on Irish Moiled cattle and in the early Thirties we had six firsts in a row with a wee Moiled cow called Close Rose. It was a great thrill for a teenager to get a first prize at Balmoral, but we never got Champion of the Show. The horse section was very strong, and though I was never a Clydesdale breeder I was reared in Derryboy which was a very dense Clydesdale district. When I was a schoolboy I remember seeing every Friday night six stallions coming down the road on their way to Newtownards. In those days it was a great sight to see two or three pairs of Clydesdales out to plough. The horsemen took great pride in their harness and they spent a lot of time polishing the brasses.

One of my clear memories is of The King's Hall being built. During that time I passed along the Lisburn Road nearly every week, and I've never seen such a forest of timber in my life. It was unforgettable.

One of the problems in the early days was lack of transport. It was nearly impossible for many smaller farmers in the more remote areas, unless they were convenient to railway stations. The bus service was sparse and rural roads were few, so the Show owes its success to the pioneering spirit of the early enthusiasts. It was very difficult, indeed nearly impossible, to transport an animal unless by train, because there were no cattle wagons. I remember buying a cow in Belfast and bringing her home in a lorry, and if she didn't go over the side, she nearly fell out of the bottom of the vehicle. Transport was a big problem in those days!

There have been many major changes, not only in farming specialisation but also in the effects of technology. Some 60 years ago there were over 30 full-time

> labourers in local farms I knew, but today there's not one. Farmers now employ full-time contractors. If industry had made as good use of technology as the farmers the national rate of unemployment would be much higher. Mind you I don't think people are any happier nowadays, nor do they have any more time because of the advantages in technology. In the old days a farmer had time to talk to his neighbours but now he waves as he passes by in the car.

A lady with what might be called an 'insider's' view of Balmoral is Mrs Maud Nicholson. She worked as a cleaner at Balmoral for many years, and witnessed some of the more memorable events in the history of the Society. She recalls:

Mrs Maud Nicholson was a loyal servant of the Society for almost sixty years until her retirement in 1990. She still keeps a keen interest in Balmoral and the office staff much appreciate the boxes of biscuits or sweets which she leaves in for them at the time of the Annual Show or at Christmas.

> My first introduction to the Showgrounds was through my mother, who used to bring me with her when I was aged around 12. This was roughly in 1928, during Mr MacRae's time, and before The King's Hall was built. I remember that instead of railings there was a corrugated iron fence round the Showgrounds. About two years later, I took over my mother's job of cleaning the offices.
>
> At that time there were two other big events each year, the Spring and Autumn sales, but the Show in May was always the big event of the year. Mother and I helped to look after the cloakrooms in those days, one of which was just inside the turnstiles at the front entrance and the other at the North Stand, which is still there today. We used to roll the coats up and store them in wooden pigeon holes. For two pence we supplied clean towels! Even before The King's Hall was built, I remember Lord and Lady Baden-Powell coming there for an inspection of the Girl Guides. I must have been only eleven years old at the time.
>
> The official opening of The King's Hall was a big event. I remember my mother and I staying up all night putting the finishing touches to the Entrance Hall which was to be opened by the Duke of Gloucester the next day. We didn't even get a glimpse of him, as we were so busy looking after the cloakroom, but I remember that I had never seen so many bowler hats in my life, and we managed to get ourselves in a bit of a muddle! We were kept very busy all day, so we forgot that we hadn't slept at all the night before. Luckily, the caterers remembered us, and sent down a basket with our lunch and tea.
>
> I have many memories of The King's Hall. I remember regular Exhibitions, including the first one which was a Radio Exhibition sponsored by the *Northern Whig* and the *Belfast Post*. Then the Ideal Home Exhibitions started, and I recall Barry's Circus with performing animals at Christmas, for a few years. Some of the boxers who appeared were famous in their day, such as Jimmy Warnock, Rinty Monaghan and "Spider" Kelly. Many famous stars made appearances there as well, and I remember Gracie Fields at Balmoral – but the nearest I got to her was preparing her dressing-room!

Gracie Fields occupied a unique position in the affections of the British people, as one of their favourite artistes. She appeared in The King's Hall on 26 October 1954.

Balmoral had great memories, but it could also be hard work. Since I was 13 or 14 I have been used to rising early and cleaning the office between 7 am and 9 am every week-day. In the early days, I used to go to Malone Primary School after I had finished cleaning the offices. I used to bring my little dog along and tie him to the turnstile while I worked. In the old days, there were two fires that had to be cleaned out and lit before any of the rest of the cleaning was done!

Over the years I made many friends at Balmoral, including the stall-holders who returned each year. The office staff have always been a pleasure to work with, and, all in all, I have happy memories of my time at Balmoral.

S Duffield Gibson, President of the Society, February 1987 – February 1990.

The Show has always had its characters. The late Duffield Gibson, a former President of the Society, recalled some of the more memorable personalities.

A man called Bob Ramsey used to show Friesians, and when he came to Balmoral he would make straight for the hens and collect a bucket of eggs, which he boiled hard. Then he would wash his cattle and afterwards sit down and eat the eggs! If you had gone round the Showgrounds at night you would have found people frying eggs, sausages and steak, and preparing all kinds of food. Many a four-course dinner was consumed, and you would have had a better meal there than in some of the hotels down town!

Then there was a Miss Stannis who used to show Dexters. One day one of her bulls only got second prize so she hit the judge with her umbrella. Sir Milne Barbour, who knew her quite well around Lisburn because she seemed to be on all the committees, came down to try to pacify her, and she knocked his hat off!

Another character was the Dowager Lady Dunleath who used to show goats. You would have found her sitting in the corner of the shed amongst her goats explaining all the finer points about the various breeds and the good points about goat's milk and you wouldn't have known who she was!

Duffield Gibson's family connection with the Society stretched away back into history. His Great Grandfather Duffield showed Ayrshires in 1848 at the old North West Show.

In the old days the predominant breeds were the Shorthorns and the Aberdeen Angus. It was only after the war that the Friesians started to take over, and the Shorthorns began to fade. There have been other changes too. It was really the landed gentry who started the Show, and in my younger days you would have

> seen all the landed gentry and bank people there in their hard hats, black coats and striped trousers, and you had to tip your cap to them. The ordinary farmers were in cloth caps. Many farmers never settled their accounts with suppliers until the Show, and the merchants were expected to buy them lunch. Then they would settle their accounts!

Col. James Cunningham was President of the Society from March 1964 to March 1967. Now well into his Nineties, he still keeps in touch with its affairs through his son Roly, a Vice President and Chairman of the Works Committee and his daughter Anna, who is a member of Council and is actively involved in the work of the Horse Committee.

Colonel James Cunningham, a former President of the Society, always had a good eye for a horse, but he was not a keen exhibitor.

> I could never bear to take a good horse to show, and maybe have to part with him. I had various horses which won the Reserve Champion of the Show on several occasions, but I was never really a Show man. I don't think that I ever showed what I thought was a really good horse – there are very few, and if you have them you don't want to part with them!

> I remember several outstanding characters. The first lady to ride astride, in my memory, was a Miss Girth who jumped two animals called Motorcar and Tank. She rode them astride at Shows after 1919. There were others who rode side saddle, the most famous being a Mrs Marshall. Another remarkable character was Sam Bailey of Newtownards who rode jumpers and showed horses. He had a mare called Meta which he trained to go down on her knees when she won a rosette, and another little thoroughbred called Victor which he bought for £24 on the first day of the Show and won £40 in prize-money, which was quite a lot then. Another character was Captain Kerr of Montalto who thought nothing of buying several horses at the Show. I remember him once telling me that he took six horses up to Dublin. There wasn't great trade, so he brought the six horses home – and six more!

Colonel Cunningham, still fresh in his 91st year, recalled first visiting Balmoral at the age of 5 with his father.

> I remember an open square of cinders and stone, with exhibition carts and horse machinery. There seemed to be lots of room, with no great crowds. There was only a little Show Jumping, and the main attraction was the animals. One of my great memories was that of the horse parade from the centre of Belfast and up the

Col. Cunningham recalls the Horse Parade as it made its way to the Showgrounds. This photograph taken at the 1934 Show illustrates the point as these immaculately prepared horses and vehicles enter the Arena.

Lisburn Road to Balmoral, with the heavy horses on the outside and the light horse on the inside. I remember looking at them from an open-top tram. Balmoral has always been a great shop-window for Ulster agriculture. It is one of the great Societies in Northern Ireland, with its ups and downs, through bad times in farming, through troublesome times in our history. It has played its part and it has done a tremendous amount of good in every way.

David Perry, a Vice President of the Society, proudly shows his Private Herd Book which contains the breeding details of the many exhibitor-bred Champions shown at Balmoral and other local shows. (Photograph: Alf McCreary)

David Perry, a Vice President of the Society and a member of Council since the Fifties recalled the Thirties.

They were very tough times, and it was coming near the Forties when things picked up. I remember in the early days when the cattle men stayed with their animals all night at Balmoral, and simply bedded down beside them. There were very few places to stay in Belfast. The drovers were not used to the big city, and some got the worse for drink. They were great characters. People went to the May Show to pick up tips and to meet one another.

David was not only a well known farmer but also an accomplished footballer who played for a number of top soccer teams, including Linfield.

I was able to play because in the mid-Thirties you could hire local men to help on the farm. A ploughman was paid £1 a week, with his food, and a cattleman was the same. The cattleman taught me more than anyone, and the ploughman knew better than I did what to do!

Willie and Elsie Fullerton have many memories of Balmoral. Mr Fullerton has been a member of Council for many years, and he and his wife are Life Members. Mrs Fullerton recalls her first day at the Show, in 1933.

It was an awful wet day, everything was nearly ruined. However, the Show has changed, over the years. In the past it was more of a social occasion. People had hardly met since the previous year, but now there is much more mobility all the year round.

Willie Fullerton, the uncle of former President William ES Fullerton who died at an early age, remembers the rigours of life on the farm when he was only nine years old.

I used to get up at 7.00 am and, with my elder brother, drove the milk cart to the local work-house, before going to school. The town children always got to their lessons early – I had to feed the pigs and cattle, there was so much to do on the farm.

Willie, who became a member of the RUAS in 1946, and joined the Council in 1969, attended many Shows, and in 1967 he and his wife were hosts to Princess Margaret and Lord Snowdon when they visited the Fullerton's farm. He says:

> It was great to see the Royal cars driving to our doorstep. Princess Margaret was very pleasant – I remember walking through the fields behind her.

William Fullerton and his wife Elsie were proud to welcome HRH Princess Margaret and Lord Snowdon at Camp Lodge, Lisburn on their way to the 1967 Royal Ulster Centenary Show.

Thomas Adams, a noted poultry exhibitor from Rathkenny (near Broughshane) became a member of the RUAS in 1947, and a member of Council in 1960. His first memory as an exhibitor goes back to 1936. He recalls:

> It was at Ballymena and I must have been about 12 years of age. I won Second prize, and I remember the judge's name – James Carrow of Loanhead, Midlothian. I believe that he was also a judge of dogs, horses and even white mice!
>
> My early connection with birds began through my uncle, who lived near Clough. Through him I met James Law, an old gentleman school teacher who showed birds. I am very fond of ducks in particular, and so much so that I have never tasted duck as part of a meal. It must be my sentimentality!
>
> Two of my favourite breeds are Indian Runners and Aylesburys. My mother bought me my first two ducks – Indian Runners – from the late WJM Robinson, one of the great men of the RUAS, who was an authority on birds, and a real gentleman. This was during the Second World War when the American troops were here, and a few days after I got the Indian Runners I decided to try them on a stream near our house. They went down the lane and on to the road, and a great row broke out. When I got to the scene I saw these two

Tommy Adams of Ballymena has been an exhibitor in the Poultry Section of Balmoral Show for almost sixty years. During that time he has shown many Champion birds such as this Black Orpington in 1990.

ducks walking across the road with their heads held high, and what do you think had happened – the ducks had done something Rommel couldn't do – they had stopped a whole convoy of American tanks which had screeched to a halt to let them cross the road!

Of course you get very fond of the birds you exhibit. I once had a lovely Aylesbury duck which was getting on in years. One night before a Show I was washing her neck with nice lukewarm water, and suddenly her head dropped in my hands – she was as dead as a dancer. That's the way it goes.

The Bamoral Show and the Society has had some great characters, like the Reverend RJ McImoyle of Dervock. He was a great sheep man and a most successful breeder. He was also great at telling yarns! There were always good stories about Balmoral – before the ET Green Hall opened there was a discussion about who would be invited. Would the invitation mention, for example, a man and his wife? James Pollock, who went on to be a popular President asked: "How would we know?" and up stood RD Best of Aghalee who said: "Mr Chairman does it really matter for the day?" That was the end of it!

I had some great times at Balmoral. One of my best years was 1962 when I helped to coach a Northern Ireland YFC judging team which came first in the Home Championships. Over the years I have won a lot of prizes, and I aimed at getting a winner out of every two birds exhibited. Every bird has its own characteristics, and you really have to own a bird and get to know it individually before you can exhibit it.

I've also been Chief Steward of the goats for many years, and away back in 1941 I won a prize at Glenarm against the competition of the landed gentry, including Lady Dunleath. I remember the goat well – she used to run with the cows but she came to a sad end – one of the cows hit her a 'dunt' and she was gone!

Sam Martin, President from February 1994 to February 1996, had a very important person accompanying him as he judged a class of horses at the Hunter Improvement Society's National Stallion Show at Newmarket in 1984. Sam met Her Majesty again in November 1995 when she invested him with an OBE for his services to equestrianism.

Sam Martin, who was President during 1994 and 1995, is a noted horse-breeder who has rubbed shoulders with Royalty, and most notably with the Queen herself. He says: "She is as knowledgeable a person about horses as I ever knew."

He first visited Balmoral in 1932.

In those days there were no side shows and no fashion shows. The catering

> was all in tents, with people sitting on forms – you could have been sitting beside anybody. I remember, too, the Hiring Fairs and going with my father to Newry. The pay was £8 for a half-year, and £16 for the year plus bed and board. You made an agreement on price, and 2 shillings or 2/6 was the bonding price. My father was a hard-worker who had little sympathy early on for my love of horses! "No more of that tom foolery", he warned, "you should be at home tying corn". Later on, however, I bought two ponies which had been 1st and 2nd at Dublin, and from that moment I was hooked!

Some breeders had their own methods of catching the judges' attention. Allen Anderson a former Chairman of the Finance Committee and President of the Society was a noted cattle exhibitor. He explains:

> Going into the ring, it was important to catch the judges' eyes and to try to enter at the moment they were looking in my direction. Sometimes people would have their own methods. A bottle of stout might be used to 'drench' an animal to make it look more lively!

A relaxed Allen Anderson who was President from December 1980 to March 1984 enjoys the excellent summer weather of 1995 with his wife Caroline. (Photograph: Alf McCreary)

Allen, and his wife Caroline, both have long memories of Balmoral Shows. He says:

> The Show has always had a real purpose. It does great service to Northern Ireland agriculture. There is always a good display of machinery, and of pedigree animals, and it does give the city folk an opportunity to have a glimpse of agriculture.

Lord O'Neill, former President and former Chairman of the Finance Committee, recalls:

The Lord O'Neill, President of the Society from March 1984 – February 1987.

> Although I had attended the Balmoral Show for a number of years beforehand, I first became actively involved in 1970 when I joined the Society as a Life Member. This came about as a result of a business association with Desmond Lorimer (now Sir Desmond), who at that time, was a partner in Harmood Banner Smylie & Co, and was responsible for the Society's finances. I joined the Council shortly afterwards and the Finance Committee in 1973, becoming Chairman in December 1974. It was at this point that I developed a close relationship with the organisation which has survived to this day, although, obviously, to a lesser degree, after I completed my Presidential term in 1987.

> I have never had strong links with any particular section of the Society, having a broad interest in farming, rather than a close association with cattle, sheep or horses. However, as a 'Museum' man, I have always had a keen interest in old agricultural machinery. I did persuade the Staff on one occasion that a demonstration of steam threshing would be an appropriate addition to the attractions. Unfortunately, the smoke, steam and flying chaff were less than popular with some of the surrounding exhibitors and therefore, it was a once-only occasion!
>
> There has been a continuing debate over the years about the ideal location for the Society. Some years ago, we did consider a green-field site within striking distance of Belfast. However, the advantages of retaining the income provided by The King's Hall could not be overlooked. Nevertheless, the site is very cramped and I sincerely hope that the current discussions about an expansion on the present site will be successful.
>
> My main impression, over some fifteen years of active involvement, is the good humour with which the Society's affairs are conducted. I cannot recall a single occasion when there were cross words at the Finance Committee or Council, although, occasionally, individuals would make a point in forthright terms. There were many occasions when one of the Society's humourists would reduce us to laughter.
>
> My other abiding memory is the long periods spent in the front row of the President's Box, both as President and Chairman of the Finance Committee. The weather was extremely variable and I distinctly remember having to vacate the front row when driving snow made it untenable on one occasion. Although my successor as President, Duffield Gibson, accused me of presiding over a wet three years, the 'wash-out' was the exception, rather than the rule.
>
> One thing one can say, without doubt, is that the Society has been a success story and has kept going throughout the 'Troubles', with only minor disruptions. It seems, therefore, that the management of the organisation has been very sound.

A man with great insight and a perceptive turn of phrase is James Pollock, who joined Council in 1951 and was President from 1990 – 92.

> I joined Council because the pig breeders were getting a poor show – I felt there was not enough attention or space given to them, so I joined to protect their interests. You could say that I was a militant! As you get older as you see how things are run, you begin to realise that other people believe that they are not getting a fair crack of the whip either! You join other committees and you realise that the Show has to run as a unit, and not just for the benefit of the pigs or the sheep or the cattle alone!

I suppose my biggest thrill was the fact that I was elected President. From being a somewhat argumentative member of several committees, they must have thought I was presentable enough to be President. I found that the President of the RUAS was well-received everywhere which was a reflection on the good name of the Society. And it was a great pleasure to meet so many people who went out of their way to help, especially after me being such a 'trouble-maker'! You might say that I'm the 'rebel' turned President.

James Pollock (President 1990-1993) was delighted to be able to welcome HRH Prince Philip to Balmoral during his term of office, the first Royal Visitor to the Showgrounds for many years. As a memento of the visit in February 1991, Prince Philip was presented with a copy of the book "This Northern Land", written by Alf McCreary and illustrated by Chris Hill.

What will happen in the future?

No-one can predict this. The changes come so quickly nowadays, but the people who run the Show have to keep a weather-eye open and try to forecast what will be best for next year, never mind 10 years hence. You cannot stand still, otherwise you go backwards. And if you don't change with the times, the times will change you.

Michael Drake, the Agriculture Editor of the *Belfast Telegraph*, casts a fond eye over Balmoral and its many characters:

My predecessor, the late, legendary 'WD', Billy Morrow told me way back in the mid-Seventies, 'You will love Balmoral at times and you will loath it at times, but every year you will go back to the May Show, for it gets into your blood.'

At that time, Spring 1976 to be precise, I took his sentiments with the proverbial pinch of salt. After all, a man leaving the scene may be forgiven for being a little subjective about it all. Since then, however, I have come to appreciate the wisdom of one who knew Balmoral, the Showgrounds and those who administered one of the 'giants' of the agri-show scene better than most. He had every reason for so doing. After all 'WD' had covered no less than thirty-three May shows and hundreds of other events at the same venue. Little did I realise, in those early years I would even attend more than a third that number.

Yes, Balmoral, the Royal Ulster, call it what you like does get in the blood. And like printer's ink it remains there for a long time. It is a place for all seasons and a Mecca for all people. Here the doyens of the dairy industry rub shoulders with the innovators from the machinery scene, the personalities of the equestrian world and visiting dignitaries. Here too the town meets the country to the benefit of both.

Mere mortals like myself observe it all, attempting to record the scene, as much for those who attend and do not see it all, as for those prevented from being present through seasonal harvesting operations and other farm chores.

The May Show, of course is only one calendar event in a year that brings thousands to the RUAS for a variety of reasons. And while I have savoured The King's Hall in its many guises – boxing arena, car showroom and pop concert venue – I will remember it best for its stands and stalls in Springtime and the excellent turnout of dairy cattle at the Winter Fair every December. Of course it would be difficult not to highlight 'figures' who dominated the scene. It would be an impossible task to mention them all. But there are individuals I will never forget.

They include James Kernohan who held the reins as Secretary Manager at the RUAS; Presidents of the calibre of Granville Nugent – a gentleman of the old school but a fine one at that – Duffield Gibson who could have discussed everything from DeLorean – the car factory was built on his land – to Long Horn cattle; the knowledgeable James Pollock, and Sam Martin, one of the finest horse breeders in these islands.

Away from the hierarchy of the place I have appreciated too the help, assistance and guidance given freely by men like Johnny Johnston and Tom 'Barney McCool' McDevitt, always eager to help with Show results; Tommy Deane who knows every square inch of the place and all the shortcuts from cattle lawn to horse arena.

More than most I continue to call on the aid of the indoor staff and never find them failing. Away from the glamour and the tumult these are the people who really make everything come true. Chief Executive Bill Yarr, Agricultural Director Lyle Rea and Commercial Director Phillip Rees and their 'powerhouse' team are the unsung heroes of the hour. The RUAS has grown well in the short time I have known it. It will continue to grow even further in the years ahead. And it will always have a place in the Province so long as agriculture is needed in Northern Ireland.

Patricia Trueman, the Chief Executive's Private Secretary, pictured (from left) with Tommy Deane (Showgrounds Manager), Lyle Rea (Agricultural Director) and Philip Rees (Commercial Director). It is a coincidence that this group between them during the Centenary Year, will have amassed a total of 100 years service with the Society.

J A W Wilberforce, RUAS Gateman, 1937.

Appendices

Appendix A

ROYAL ULSTER AGRICULTURAL SOCIETY PATRONS

1886 – 1888	His Excellency The Marquis of Londonderry
1889 – 1891	His Excellency The Earl of Zetland
1892 – 1894	His Excellency Lord Houghton
1895 – 1901	His Excellency Earl Cadogan KG
1902 – 1905	His Excellency The Earl of Dudley
1906 – 1913	His Excellency The Earl of Aberdeen
1914	His Excellency Lord Wimborne
1915	His Excellency The Earl of Aberdeen
1916 – 1918	His Excellency Lord Wimborne
1919 – 1921	His Excellency Viscount French KP
1922	His Excellency Viscount Fitzalan
1923	No Appointment
1924 – 1944	His Grace The Duke of Abercorn KG KP
1945 – 1951	Vice Admiral The Earl Granville KCVO CB DSO LLD
1952 – 1963	The Rt Hon Lord Wakehurst KG KCMG LLD
1954 – 1968	Lord Erskine of Rerrick GBE LLD
1969 – 1973	Lord Grey of Naunton GCMG KCVO OBE LLD
1974 – 1989	No Appointment
1990 – 1995	His Grace The Duke of Abercorn
1996	HRH Prince Philip The Duke of Edinburgh

Prior to partition in 1922, the office of Patron was filled by the Lord Lieutenant of Ireland for the time being. Subsequently, the office was filled by the Governor of Northern Ireland until 1973 when the Governorship was abolished.

Appendix B

ROYAL ULSTER AGRICULTURAL SOCIETY PRESIDENTS

1855 – 1867	Marquis of Downshire
1868 – 1875	Lord Lurgan KP
1876 – 1888	General Viscount Templeton KCB
1889 – 1913	Marquis of Londonderry KG KP
1914 – 1922	Colonel The Rt Hon R G Sharman Crawford CBE DL
1923 – 1930	Rt Hon Sir Milne Barbour [see also 1933]
1931 – 1932	Captain J L Chichester-Clark DSO MP
1933 – 1951	Rt Hon Sir Milne Barbour
1952 – 1963	Lt Col The Rt Hon Sir Alex RG Gordon GBE DSO DL
1964 – Mar 1967	Lt Col James G Cunningham OBE VL
Mar 1967 – Mar 1970	Joseph M Thompson JP
Mar 1970 – Mar 1973	Major John Corbett DL JP
Mar 1973 – Mar 1976	Rt Hon The Lord Dunleath TD DL
Mar 1976 – Mar 1980	Granville C Nugent
Mar 1980 – Oct 1980	Fred W Price JP [Died 18 October 1980]
Dec 1980 – Mar 1984	Allen W Anderson JP
Mar 1984 – Feb 1987	Rt Hon The Lord O'Neill TD DL
Feb 1987 – Feb 1990	S Duffield Gibson JP
Feb 1990 – Jan 1993	James Pollock
Jan 1993 – Oct 1993	William E S Fullerton [Died 21 October 1993]
Feb 1994 – Feb 1996	Samuel R Martin OBE
Feb 1996 –	J L Courtenay Thompson

Appendix C

Royal Ulster Agricultural Society Secretary/Managers
[Chief Executive & Secretary from 1978]

		Service
1855 – 1857	John Borthwick [Hon Secretary]	3 Years
1858 – 1893	George G Bingham	35 Years
1893 – 1897	Hugh C Kelly	4 Years
1897 – 1930	Kenneth MacRae	33 Years
1930 – May 1958	Sam Clarke MBE	28 Years
May 1958 – Aug 1978	James T Kernohan OBE	20 Years
Aug 1978 –	William H Yarr OBE	

Appendix D

ROYAL ULSTER AGRICULTURAL SOCIETY
OFFICERS FOR 1996

PATRON	HRH Prince Philip The Duke of Edinburgh
PRESIDENT	J L Courtenay Thompson
DEPUTY PRESIDENT	Robin H Wylie
PAST PRESIDENTS	Allen W Anderson JP
	Col James G Cunningham OBE DL
	Rt Hon The Lord O'Neill TD
	James Pollock
	Samuel R Martin OBE

VICE PRESIDENTS

[Due to retire February 1997]

Mrs J A Collinson
Frank Dickson
John K Lynn CBE JP
Dr James A Young CB

[Due to retire February 1998]

John Gabbie
Brian T King
John D Templeton JP
H S Crosbie Cochrane OBE

[Due to retire February 1999]

Roland G Cunningham
Wilson Irvine CBE
Mrs Anne F Mark DL
Robin H Wylie

[Due to retire February 2000]

Houston L Brown
Rt Hon The Lord Lowry
John B Mills
W David Perry

The Body Corporate of the Society is the Council who meet on six occasions during the year to receive reports from the various Committees. After the October 1995 meeting, those present gathered on the balcony of The King's Hall. The President, Sam Martin, is seen wearing the chain and Badge of Office. Also included are the three members of the Senior Management Team.

Appendix E

ROYAL ULSTER AGRICULTURAL SOCIETY
COUNCIL AS AT 2 FEBRUARY 1996
The Council consists of the President, Past Presidents, Vice Presidents and the following elected members

Retire Annual Meeting February 1997	Retire Annual Meeting February 1998	Retire Annual Meeting February 1999
John Allen	Thomas Adams	Mrs Christine Adams
Richard S F Armour	James Armstrong JP	Edwin Adams
Sam Black	John Bamber	W J Armstrong
Stephen Brann	Crosby Cleland	The Lady Dunleath
Robert Campbell	R J T Duddy JP	J Hall Fraser
James Coburn	Thomas Gibson	William Fullerton JP
Harry Crawford	C John Henning	George Hamilton
Hugh M Ferguson	John G Kelly	Robert Harkness
Hubert Gabbie	James B Kirk	W J Henning MBE DL JP
Dr S A Noel Greer	H Wilson Logan	Thomas A Larmour
Dr Ernest F Logan	Mrs Jean Mann	Thomas G Lindsay
Alfred E Martin	Samuel Marsden	James A Logan
Timothy Martin	John C Martin	A H Stewart Moore JP
Robert Morrow	William R Martin JP	W Robin Morrow CBE
Sam K McCausland	Maurice N Megahey	Michael M Murray
Robert J McConnell	Cyril M Millar	John B MacMillan
J Wilson McCracken	James McV Morrison	Terence McKeag JP
John McMordie	Norman C McClelland	Wilby McKee
John B Robinson	Robert Overend JP	C E Suffern
Walter G Smyth OBE	J Austin Perry	Sam Torrens CBE
Mrs D G Thompson	Hugh Rankin	John Warden
J Craig Wallace MBE	Wilbert E Rankin	Rev W J Watson MBE
Eric Williamson	William H Robson OBE	T Gordon West
Samuel J Wilson	Norman P Sloan	

APPOINTED BY THE DEPARTMENT OF AGRICULTURE NORTHERN IRELAND

J W Duff H R Kirkpatrick John Murray CB Dr R M McCracken S J McGaughey

Appendix F

TYRONE CRYSTAL PERPETUAL PLATE

The Tyrone Crystal Perpetual Plate was presented to the Society in 1991 and Council agreed that it should be awarded annually to a Member having made a significant contribution towards the work of the Society.

The Plate is displayed throughout the year in the Cup Cabinet in the foyer of the Balmoral Conference Centre with the winner retaining a smaller sized replica.

Winners to date have been:–

1991	John B Anderson
1992	John B Mills
1993	John Gabbie
1994	Mrs Margaret Collinson
1995	Robin H Wylie

Mrs Margaret Collinson, the recipient of the Tyrone Crystal Plate for 1994, received the award from Mrs Winnie Corr of Tyrone Crystal Ltd at the Annual Meeting in February 1995. Also included is S R Martin wearing the Presidential Badge of Office which was worn officially for the first time, having been presented to the Society at the same meeting through an anonymous donor. A splendid chain was also presented to be worn on more formal occasions.

Appendix G

ROYAL ULSTER AGRICULTURAL SOCIETY
MANAGERIAL, ADMINISTRATIVE AND SHOWGROUNDS STAFF
at 1 January 1996:–

Mrs Margaret Armstrong
David Browne
Mrs Paula Clendinning
Kenny Coyle
Ernie Culbert
Mrs Marty Cullum
Paul Cunningham
Tommy Deane
Miss Rhonda Duncan
Oliver Egan
Trevor Evans
Freddie Ferguson
Robbie Hanna
Mrs Karen Hughes
Tommy Knox
George Megaw
Mrs Sonya Mills
Ms Lucy Moore
Mrs Elizabeth McCullagh
Ms Belinda McFadden
T Lyle Rea
Philip M Rees
Miss Patricia Trueman
William H Yarr

The day to day work of the Society is undertaken by the managerial, administrative and grounds staff who were photographed together in front of the Balmoral Conference Centre in September 1995.